C000038252

From Highlights to Lowlifes

by Alyson Chattoe and Jilly Clark

Copyright © 2017 Alyson Chattoe and Jilly Clark

The rights of Alyson Chattoe and Jilly Clark to be identified as the authors of this work have been asserted in accordance with the Copyright, Designs and Patents Act 1988. All rights reserved.

Published by TWH Publishing;
Independent Publishing House, West Yorkshire
www.thewritinghall.co.uk

Cover design by Charlie O'Neill;
www.sebandcharliedesign.co.uk

Except for the quotation of small passages for the purposes of criticism and review, no part of this publication may be reproduced, stored in a retrieval system, or transmitted, in any form or by any means, electronic, mechanical, photocopying, recording or otherwise, except under the terms of the Copyright, Designs and Patents Act 1988, and without the prior consent of the publisher.

This book is a work of fiction and, except in the case of historical fact, any resemblance to actual persons, living or dead, is purely coincidental. A record of this book is available from the British Library.

ISBN 978-0-9934767-9-2

Printed in the UK by Grosvenor Group Ltd, Loughton, Essex IG10 3TS

Alyson:

To Andrew - you care, you listen, you understand, and you make me laugh out loud.

Jilly:

To my loving mum and dad, for their constant support. I could not have survived without it.

To my three wonderful children who love me unconditionally, and who have never judged me - and who, no matter what, are always there for me.

Acknowledgements

Alyson:

Jilly, thank you for giving me this opportunity to ghost-write your life story. You gave me full access to your diary, you enthusiastically answered all my questions, and relayed graphic accounts of the horrors you endured in prison. You're always candid and positive, and you have become a good friend.

Diane, your professionalism, your encouragement, and your belief in me - even when I did not believe in myself - has boosted my confidence no end. Talk about being in the right place at the right time. You always give good advice and sound, constructive feedback. You have a natural flair for writing, which I admire no end. It is a privilege to know you.

Jilly:

Heartfelt thanks to Jane Walton - for your inspiration and friendship, and for your steadfast belief in my story. You laid the foundations, and introduced me to Diane.

To Alyson, who I've always believed in. Thank you for ghost-writing this book, and for your wonderful friendship.

To Diane; thanks for your patience, understanding, and positive attitude - especially during our frequent meetings. Your creativity and expertise have guided us through this incredible journey.

Chapter One

As I drove the hire car towards the ferry, I felt on edge and couldn't relax. It was nerve-wracking, though there was no indication things wouldn't go to plan. I'd been given everything I needed the previous night. The meeting had gone without incident, better than I'd expected - not that I really knew what to expect.

I'd never done anything like that before. *And I didn't chicken out. I've achieved what I set out to do.* I tried to convince myself that this was the only solution.

I turned my attention to the road. I had plenty of time. Calais drew near, and the ferry that would take me home. I had to keep checking I was on the 'wrong' side of the road. My mind conjured up all sorts of thoughts; it was a struggle to concentrate. *It will all be worthwhile. Just a few more miles - or is it kilometres when you're in France? Who really cares?* I felt myself becoming agitated and tried to think of nothing but the drive.

I was glad that I'd worn a light knitted jumper and jeans: comfy clothing for travelling, like any casual tourist. *That's exactly how you have to look, stupid woman! Especially when you get on the ferry.* My brain continued to spout rubbish.

It was a cool Friday morning, around six o'clock. The sun was just rising. *It's going to be another hot August day.* I was glad it was Bank Holiday week-end; loads of people would be travelling to and from France. Perfect conditions. I'd blend into the masses.

Thinking of my life just a few months ago, I couldn't believe how messed up it had become. I was a successful businesswoman, once upon a time, with my own hairdressing salon. I'd built up a good clientele and had a good life. *Is 'clientele' a French term? Does it really matter? God help me, my brain is overloading!* It wouldn't be long before I reached the port. My bladder told me I needed the loo. That led to me think again: *what the hell am I doing?*

I managed to appear reasonably normal as I queued to get on the ferry. If anything, I was bored. I kept looking at my watch. *Just a couple of hours and I'll be in Dover.* Then, it'd be a few more hours at the wheel to get home. It made me tired, thinking of the long drive ahead. Still, I was capable, it wasn't a big deal. I could stop for coffee and something to eat at service stations, then have a good rest back home. I began to feel more positive.

A member of the ferry staff waved me towards a space and I parked the car. I was on a lower deck than when I'd gone out to France. *Did that matter?* I wished my brain would stop questioning everything.

I felt shaky and jumped at the slightest thing. *It's because I'm tired and hungry. Or is it nerves?* It could even have been down to the petrol and diesel fumes flooding the air as more cars parked up.

I hurried up the stairs to get to the toilet before I wet myself. Once in a cubicle, and with great relief, I let the floodgates open. I sat there for some time, even though it smelt rancid. I knew women were queuing outside, but I couldn't have cared less. I needed time to gather my thoughts without anyone bothering me.

From leaving the solitude of the car, it had suddenly spooked me, being around a lot of people. I felt paranoid. I couldn't make myself move; I just sat there, listening to the annoyingly loud chatter, the water running, the hand dryers operating. *Maybe I'll still be sitting here when we arrive at Dover...*

I'd always considered myself a confident woman and an optimist, but sat there, I felt the opposite. I knew my strengths and weaknesses; I knew I suffered from anxiety. At the start of the journey, I'd been resigned to the thought it was necessary. I'd felt confident I could carry it out. *Easier said than done.* Now I was here, actually doing it, I questioned myself.

What was I doing? Think, girl, of the upside...half the journey's over. Soon, all your troubles will be over and you can get your life back to how it was.

Justification was easy. It was what I needed to do to carry on. I thought of my wonderful children: my boy and girl from my first marriage; now, young adults with lovely personalities, opinions and attitudes. And my youngest - the product of my second relationship. He was young but clever. Seven going-on thirty, and full of energy. This time round, I was convinced my partner was the love of my life.

I put my head in my hands and prayed that I'd soon be home with them all, and that this ordeal would be behind me.

I'd never felt so alone. *But it was all in a good cause, wasn't it? I couldn't lose what I had, just because of someone else's mistakes. I had to fight to keep it.* A wildlife programme I'd watched some weeks ago came to mind. In nature, a mother will do anything for her young. Who was I kidding? This was for them, but it was my decision. I wanted to keep the life I'd become accustomed to.

I adjusted the package strapped to my midriff; it was becoming loose, and my skin felt warm and itchy underneath it. I daren't remove it, so I vigorously scratched the skin beneath. I pulled the package as tight as I could to my stomach, making sure it was secure and wouldn't slip. I decided to put a sanitary towel over the top, to help tape it to my body.

I pulled down my jumper, got off the toilet and pulled up my knickers and jeans. I felt that if I didn't move then I never would. I flushed the toilet, grabbed my handbag, and walked out of the cubicle, feeling as if everyone was looking at me because I'd been in there for so long. I joined the throng of women trying to get to the sink, so I could wash my hands. I seemed to move in slow motion, whilst everyone around me was on fast forward. Their noise clanged in my ears.

I took deep breaths to calm down, and started to wash my hands. I pushed hard on the soap dispenser and literally wrung them, like a surgeon scrubbing up before an operation. I looked round quickly. *Everyone's watching me...* I had to get a grip. I tried to act normal. I rinsed my hands then glanced in the mirror. *I look so stressed.*

I dried my hands then moved to a different mirror and took out a lipstick. My favourite cherry-red. I tried to apply it but my hands were shaking so much, I gave up before anyone noticed. Instead, I took a brush from my bag and combed my hair.

My reflection stared back at me. I looked like a rabbit caught in headlights. *Where's the defiant sparkle I usually see?* I needed the hardcore part of me to come to the surface, to keep me sane.

With my short, trendy hairstyle and manicured nails, I could have passed for thirty-five, under normal circumstances, rather than forty-two. The person in the mirror looked much, much older.

I became aware that the ferry had set off. A wave of nausea washed over me. I was usually a good traveller; sea, plane or car. It was probably because I hadn't eaten for some time. I needed to get some food, some inner fuel.

I slowly made my way to the restaurant area. The smell of food hit me like a mallet. I hadn't realised how hungry I was.

I felt watched again. *Is it because I'm on my own? Shall I pretend to look for a companion?* I glanced as casually as I could around the room, checking there were no officials approaching. I kept holding my breath. *What's that all about?*

I got in line, took a plastic tray, and looked at the food on offer. I picked up a bottle of water; I had to remain hydrated. Croissants, ham, cheese, salami. *Is that what these foreigners think breakfast is?* I finally got to the end of the counter where there was hot, greasy food on offer. I ordered eggs, bacon, sausage, tomatoes, fried bread, toast and mushrooms. At the drinks area, I couldn't decide what to have. I should really have chosen tea, but I needed caffeine. I poured a coffee, and took the plate of food to the till.

The old lady at the till looked as bored as anyone could. I fumbled for my purse. *Did they take sterling, or did I have to pay in francs? Did I even have enough in francs? Oh, just pay! Stop obsessing over stupid things.*

The old dear accepted my English money; I took my tray and walked as best I could to a seat. I moved the plate from the tray onto the table-top, put the coffee cup to my right side, then placed the tray on the opposite side of the table, as no one was sat there. I hoped this would indicate to anyone passing that they needn't join me.

I'd forgotten to get a knife and fork; they were on a central counter. Sometimes, I hated the modern world. *Whatever happened to waiter service? Jesus, who do I think I am? Just walk over and get the bloody stuff.*

I collected what I needed and returned to the table. By this point, the fry-up didn't look so good. I sat down and took a deep breath. I really didn't want to be at this precise spot at this precise time.

I picked up the cutlery. A voice at the back of my mind said, 'Eat, eat, eat!' I cut up the sausage before slicing into the egg. I watched the runny yolk spill across the plate. I raised the fork to my mouth then slowly lowered it back to the plate. I picked up the coffee cup instead and took a sip.

I couldn't eat. My appetite had gone. I should eat, I needed to eat. But how could I? I knew if I took even a mouthful I'd throw it back up. *I can always eat when I get to Dover.* I decided to have a cigarette; nicotine would calm me down, and hopefully, I'd stop drawing attention to myself.

I got out my cigarettes and lighter and relished the hit as I lit it. I sipped the coffee and felt stronger. I pushed the plate of food to the opposite side of the table. *Forget it, it's only food. I'll have a good fry-up when I get home.* I really enjoyed the cigarette, and lit another as soon as I'd stubbed the first one out. I'd finished the coffee by this time, and hankered after another cup. Instead, I drank two-thirds of the bottle of water. *At this rate, I'll be back to the toilet.*

I decided to buy some more water before I left the restaurant. Then I slowly made my way to the top deck, lit another cigarette, and tried to look casual.

I enjoyed the heat of the sun on my skin, and the sea breeze reminded me to breathe. I watched the waves for a few minutes. They were mesmerising, and it gave me the chance to just 'be'; no thoughts, just peace.

The feeling didn't last long. A woman nudged me. 'Got a light?' I jumped a mile at her touch; I was convinced she wanted something else. I glanced quickly around the deck. It was filled with families, couples and staff, all milling about, just getting on with their day. *Why am I so paranoid? No one knows what's strapped to my body.*

It was clear the young woman just wanted a light, so I obliged. She took a long drag, satisfaction written all over her face, before handing back the lighter.

'Thanks. I'm trying to stop, but the urge is too strong today. I bought a pack but forgot to get some matches. It's my first packet in six weeks.'

I smiled. 'I wish I could stop. They're too expensive to buy these days.'

She started to say something, but stopped as I yelped. Someone had slapped my back. I hurriedly turned round.

'Hi, Tilly! Fancy seeing you here.'

Oh my God. What? No, No... Think! Stood in front of me, to my horror, were friends of the family: Ron, and his wife, Dorothy. *This isn't happening! What the hell?!*

Dorothy smiled at me and moved in for a hug. She kissed me on both cheeks. I just stood there, rigid. She drew back. 'What's wrong? Are you alright?' I just nodded. 'So, who are you with? Have you been on holiday, too?'

I looked at her, then to Ron, dumbstruck. My mind had gone blank. A few seconds passed before I cleared my throat and was able to speak. 'Well...hello! How are you? You look well, have you been on holiday?' I hoped to God they'd start talking about their trip so I'd have time to think of something credible to say. I watched the woman who'd borrowed my lighter walk away.

Dorothy had been at school with my mother – I'd known the couple all my life. Mum and Dad spent time with them regularly. And I'd gone to school with their kids. What a nightmare. 'Come on, let's get a coffee and catch up,' said Ron. I didn't know what to do as they started walking towards the restaurant. Reluctantly, I followed them, my legs shaking.

We sat down with coffees. For a few moments, conversation stopped as we politely sipped our drinks. Dorothy was a petite woman; slim, with a long face and an elongated nose. Her bulging eyes were a deep blue. Every week, I'd shampoo and set her permed, greying hair.

Ron was also slim, but much taller, at least six foot. His hair was like a grey curtain, circling his head from ear to ear whilst the rest of his head was bald. He wore thick-rimmed, black-framed glasses. The shape of his face seemed to defy his slim physique; he had floppy, bulbous cheeks. I'd once heard someone call him 'bollock chops' behind his back. Ron had a kind nature, and was usually the life and soul of any get-together.

We talked for a while, and I hoped I'd convinced them that I was coming back from a friend's wedding. 'A friend travelled with me on the outward journey, but she's decided to stay for the week. That's why I'm on my own.' They both nodded.

'Did Jake not want to go to the wedding?' said Dorothy.

'No. Er, he's at home, looking after Elliot. He didn't know anyone going to the wedding, so he wasn't bothered about coming,' I babbled.

I asked about their holiday, even though I wasn't the slightest bit interested, in the hope they'd stop asking me questions. 'You've both got lovely tans,' I said. 'How's the family?' Whilst I didn't think Ron thought there was anything odd about me, I felt Dorothy eyeing me suspiciously.

I was shocked at how old she looked, from when I'd last seen her. Her lined face looked ashen and was more heavily creased, and she seemed subdued. She started relaying news of the family, and talked about their holiday, which lasted about an hour. When she stopped, I felt myself blushing and tears pricked my eyes. I looked over at Ron, who was looking down into his coffee.

I could feel myself hotting up. Nausea swamped me.

I excused myself to go to the bathroom, blaming sea-sickness. Ron smiled. 'We're going to duty free.'

'I'll probably join you later,' I said shakily.

I practically ran to the toilets. Once inside a cubicle, I felt safe. *This is not who I am.* I felt terrible, lying to Dorothy.

I need to get home. The journey seemed to take forever. I looked at my watch. *Not long now.* In about thirty minutes we'd dock at Dover.

I tried to shake off the sick feeling; I needed to be in control. I checked the damned package again, left the cubicle, and headed to the car - whilst trying to avoid everyone.

In the vehicle, on the verge of disembarking, I felt a surge of relief. The worst part of the journey was over. There was a long drive ahead, but then I'd be home.

I drove off the ferry and towards customs. My mouth felt dry, and my hands gripped the steering wheel. I carefully manoeuvred the car into the 'Nothing to Declare' corridor. As I slowed, six customs officers walked towards my car. They indicated for me to move to the slip road at the side.

My heart started pounding. Then all hell broke loose.

Chapter Two

The nearest customs officer opened the car door. 'Please turn off the engine and get out of the car, madam.'

I looked up at him but couldn't find any words. I picked up my handbag, and slowly got out of the car. *Shit!*

I seemed to be surrounded; there were officers all over the car. One escorted me to a low wall. 'Sit here while we search your car.' I did as I was told.

He asked me for my passport. I fumbled in my handbag, and with trembling hands, handed it over.

'What's the purpose of your visit?' he asked.

I tried to reply as casually as I could. 'Sightseeing. A booze and cigarette run.' He nodded, and started to flick through the pages of my passport.

I looked away, trying not to think about what was happening. I watched as a sniffer dog was led to the car. It bounced about the front seats, sniffed over the dashboard, and inspected the foot wells. It then turned its attention to the front inner door panels before eventually jumping out. The handler instructed the dog to repeat the process in the back of the car.

I saw three men with tool-boxes walking towards the car. They started to take it apart. In a weird way, it was fascinating - how quickly they did it. To the mechanics, it was child's play, like they were messing about with Meccano.

I knew they'd not find anything in the vehicle. I'd hired the car myself, and I'd been forced to park a few streets away from the address I'd been given. The place where I was given the package.

I prayed for the floor to open and swallow me up. My bum started to get cold; my first thought was that I'd wet my pants, but I realised it was the stone wall I

11

could feel through my jeans.

I was sweating yet shivering at the same time. The sun seemed to single me out with its hot rays. I looked down and noticed that I'd wrapped my arms across my stomach, as if I was subconsciously trying to push the package through my skin.

I put my hands on the wall and sat up straighter, in a bid to appear normal. I wished my heart rate would slow down; it thumped against my chest - I could hear its rapid rhythm in my ears. Every other sound was muted.

A shadow passed over me. I squinted as I looked upwards. The officer stood over me was talking, but I only noticed his mouth opening and closing. The sun was so bright, I raised my hand to shield my eyes from the glare.

My senses were in overdrive. I heard the seagulls screeching, cars revving, drills whirring, metal banging, people talking, and the gentle waves lapping against the quay. I smelled car fumes, the salty sea air, and a stale fishy odour, which immediately brought bile to the back of my throat. Cars passed by, and birds glided on the breeze. *God, if only I could fly...* I started to shake, and swallowed down the acrid bile.

'Are you alright, Mrs. McVeigh?' I heard the officer ask.

'I feel sick. I think I ate something dodgy last night. I haven't felt good all morning,' I managed to reply.

At that moment the sniffer dog came over. Without thinking, I bent down to pat it. The handler suddenly shouted, 'Back!' His voice was so commanding and loud, it made me jump with fright. The dog ran back. The two officers exchanged glances. One nodded to the other.

I looked at the dog sat at the side of its handler. It

was a beautiful spaniel - white, with brown liver spots. Its tail was wagging and its tongue dangled from the side of its mouth. The handler put down a bowl of water. It dawned on me that I was smiling; I loved dogs. I had one at home that was spoilt rotten. And now this beautiful animal had just given me away.

'Mrs. McVeigh, please come with me to the office.' Reluctantly, I followed the officer, my head down. 'Please take a seat,' he said, when we entered the room. 'Would you like a drink?'

'Could I have a coffee, please? Is it okay if I smoke in here?' The officer nodded.

The room was bright, and it had a table to one side with four chairs around it. Down the other side of the room was a saggy-looking sofa and a filing cabinet in the corner.

'I'll organise coffee. Take a seat,' said the officer. I sat down at the table and took my lighter and cigarettes from my handbag.

A younger officer brought in a tray; he smiled at me as I took a cup of coffee. There was also a plate of biscuits. I remembered that I'd not had anything to eat and took one. I had a bite then took a drag of my cigarette. *What am I doing?! I'm not with friends in a café!*

I put down the biscuit and just drank the coffee. The customs officer came back with my passport. He sat opposite me. 'Are you feeling better, Mrs. McVeigh?'

'Yes, thank you.'

'I'm Officer Talbot. I'm the senior officer in charge. In a few minutes, you'll be taken to a holding cell for a body search, which will be carried out by a female officer. We have reason to believe you're concealing drugs on your person. If this is found to be the case, you will be formally arrested, appointed a solicitor, then interviewed. I suggest you fully cooperate.' I just stared at him. 'Do you understand what I've just said, Mrs. McVeigh?'

My eyes stung and tears poured down my face. I nodded. 'Can I ring home? They expect me home this afternoon.'

'We'll need to search you first. When you've been appointed a solicitor, you can ring home.'

It wasn't long before I was in the holding cell with two female officers. One of them simply stood and watched, saying nothing.

The other barked orders. 'Stand with your legs apart. Arms spread out.' I did as she asked and she patted me down. 'Lift your jumper up, so I can see what you have strapped to your body.'

For a moment I froze, then slowly I raised the hem of my top.

She started to peel away the tape to remove the package. It stung a little, but it came off relatively easily - probably because I was sweating profusely. 'This package will now be taken for analysis. In the meantime, we need to examine your clothes.' She left the room.

I looked at the other officer. 'You need to take off all your clothes and put them in there.' She pointed to a bag on the bed of the cell. *God, this is too much!* She opened a drawer, took something out and thrusted it towards me. 'Put this on.' She placed what looked like mechanics' overalls on the bed.

Still crying, I unfolded the all-in-one jumpsuit. Boots were attached to the end of the trouser legs. I self-consciously undressed then picked up the suit; it was at least three sizes too big. Being only five feet two inches tall, the garment was better suited to a giant. I zipped up the front; the crotch was level with my knees. *Is this to humiliate me?* If so, it was bloody working. I folded my clothes to put them in the bag, and noticed a small amount of blood on the inside of my jeans. *That's all I need, my fucking period! No wonder I feel shit.* 'Can I go to the toilet?' I asked.

'Use the toilet in the corner.'

I walked towards it and paused. She didn't move a muscle. *She's going to stay and watch me pee?!*

I looked again at the toilet bowl; it looked odd. I sat down on the toilet. It seemed to take ages before I allowed my body to let go. I got up and flushed the loo; the water seemed to go straight through the wall instead of downwards. Then it struck me. *They must have to inspect everything that goes into the loo, somewhere on the other side of that wall. What sort of job is that?*

I felt like a shrunken astronaut, shuffling in the large boots. I was led into another office. This one had a computer and a phone on the desk, and quite a lot of paperwork across it. Officer Talbot was sat behind the desk at first, then he got up and walked over to me, his hand outstretched, offering me a tissue. He indicated for me to take a seat, then passed me a small glass of water. I sipped as he talked, then realised he was formally arresting me. *Oh my God, I can't believe I've been so stupid.*

Officer Talbot read me my rights. He charged me with smuggling class 'A' drugs into the UK. 'You've been appointed a duty solicitor. You'll meet them soon.'

By now, I was sobbing uncontrollably and struggling to catch my breath. I was aware that snot was running down my face. I tried to cover my face with the tissue, in a futile attempt to hide. *I can't take this. I'm not strong enough.*

'Mrs. McVeigh...may I call you Tilly? Is that short

for Matilda? Natalie?'

My face was still buried in the tissue. 'No, it's just Tilly,' I mumbled.

'Try and calm down. We'll assist you as best we can in this situation.'

I wiped my nose and tried to control my breathing. He looked at me with genuine concern; in fact, he looked positively sorry for me. 'You're going to go back into the holding cell while we organise a doctor to carry out an internal examination. We can apply for a warrant for this procedure, but you can give your consent for this to be done without a warrant...which will go in your favour. By consenting, it can be carried out sooner rather than later."

'Get the doctor. I'll agree to everything. Just get it over with.'

'Okay. Some food has been organised for you. Please eat, it will make you feel better.'

I felt like saying, 'Who do you think you are? My mother?!' Instead, I kept quiet.

In the cell, I was still sobbing when the food arrived. It resembled a tray of food you'd get on an aeroplane, but I was on no holiday. The irony would normally have made me smile, except all I could do was cry. I looked at my watch; it was 11.30am. On auto-pilot, I unwrapped the bread bun, buttered it and chewed. It seemed to take me hours to finish the food; I'd take a bite, blow my nose, wipe away the tears, then swallow. Though, I admit, I enjoyed the cup of coffee.

Left on my own, I started to feel a little calmer. Until I looked at the garb I was wearing; I looked like Herman Munster. At least no-one was staring at me, making me feel like a criminal. *But I am a criminal.* This scenario had never, ever entered my head. *How stupid am I? What made me think I could get away with smuggling drugs?* More tears.

A female nurse entered the cell, with one of the female officers. 'Hello. I'm Nancy. If you come with me, the doctor is ready to examine you.'

I gave a weak smile and tentatively followed her into a room where everything was made of steel. It covered every surface - even the tables were made of steel. *Is this where they do autopsies?* Some of the tables had gutter-like channels down their sides. I assumed that was where the blood went. *Gross.*

The doctor introduced himself, then asked me to undress and lay on the table, where he would examine me. I became hysterical again. 'Please, please, just examine me at the front. Please do not go up my back passage.' As the words came out, I knew I sounded like a little kid. I couldn't imagine anything going up my backside.

In a snotty tone, he said, 'As part of an internal inspection, I need to be sure you do not have any drugs in both cavities.'

I nearly screamed. 'Please, doctor! I promise, truly promise, I have not got anything up me anywhere. Please, not the back. Please!' I wailed.

The doctor took note of my state and relented. 'You're obviously very distressed. I'll just examine your vagina.'

I thanked him, as if he was doing me a huge favour. I didn't bother to tell him I was menstruating – he'd soon find that out for himself. After undressing, I climbed onto the table. Laying on the cold steel, my legs spread and naked, I felt like a piece of meat.

Back in the holding cell, I was given my own clothes to put on. I felt more human with knickers on and a sanitary towel; at least I wasn't leaking, feeling dirty, like when I wore the suit. *I'm so exhausted.*

I was taken to the interview room. The Duty Solicitor, Mr. Hewitt, introduced himself. He looked decent enough. He spoke kindly to me, and explained the interviewing process...if I needed any breaks, etc. He pointed out that, in the circumstances, I should admit to everything. Down the track, this would help me.

'How long after the interview will it be before I can go home? I always take my grandma shopping on a Saturday.'

He must have thought I was thick. 'Sorry, Tilly, you won't be going home. You're being charged with a very serious crime. You'll be put into a cell tonight, and tomorrow, you'll go to Holloway Prison.' It felt like the solicitor had punched me in the face, such was the impact of his words.

He continued, 'Holloway is a top security remand prison, that mainly deals with serious crimes. It's the nearest.' He softened. 'You'll go there until the hearing for a court date.'

I could only imagine my expression resembled a scared rabbit caught by headlights. 'You're allowed a phone call,' he added. 'Would you like to phone home before the interview starts...talk to your family? I'm sure you need to speak to them.'

I followed Mr. Hewitt into a side room. It looked to be a recreation room. It had a pool table and a dart board hanging on the opposite wall. A record player and a television were in the corner. What looked like a counter or bar was down one side of the room and there were a few tables and chairs dotted around. On the counter was a telephone. 'Just dial nine to get an outside line. I'll wait over there.' He pointed to a table near the door.

Does he think I'll do a runner? Giver over, he's just trying to be helpful. It's not his fault I'm in this mess. I sat for a moment, trying to think. I'd told Jake I was on a girls' night out, staying over at a friend's house for the night - returning home Saturday morning. He had no idea what I was up to. How am I going to explain this? Slowly, I picked up the phone and dialled home.

It rang three times before Jake picked up. 'Hello?' He sounded angry.

I cleared my throat. 'Hi, Jake,' I whispered, 'it's me.'

'Tilly? What the fuck have you done? The police have been here, searching the house. They say you've been arrested for bringing drugs into the country,' he shouted.

I started sobbing. 'Jake, I have been arrested. When did the police arrive? Was our boy in the house when they came?'

Jake fell silent for a moment. 'Yes, he was in his bedroom. I took him over to next door's until they'd finished. They even searched his room, Tilly. What have you done? I can't believe this is happening.'

'I can't believe it either. You're right, this shouldn't be happening. I'll be interviewed soon and then transported to...' My voice broke. I was trying to be brave but couldn't carry it off. '...Holloway. I don't know when I can speak to you again, or if I can get in touch with Mum and Dad.'

'Jesus, Tilly,' he said, though his voice was softer now.

I felt as if I was choking. I started coughing, trying to speak. 'Could you let my family know?' I whispered.

I saw Mr. Hewitt walking over. 'It's time, Tilly,' he said.

I swallowed my sobs. 'Got to go, Jake.' As I put the phone down, I felt as if my life was over.

The horrors just kept coming. In a room, being interviewed with the tape running, I looked round at everyone present. I now understood what it means when people say they have an out of body experience. I spoke, but it wasn't my voice. I admitted everything

and answered every question just to get through it.
A couple of hours passed. Eventually, I signed a statement. *This nightmare is going round and round.* The
interview finished and handcuffs were slapped on my
wrists.

Everything was a blur. 'I'm sorry you're here, Tilly,'
said Officer Talbot. 'I wish we'd not stopped you - I'll
take this case home with me. You don't belong here,
you're not the typical criminal. Anyone can see you've
never been in trouble before.'

Looking at the cuffs through cascading tears, I
couldn't reply. As I was walked outside I felt that the
day would never end. I took in my surroundings: the
deep blue sky, the low, large sun, the white clouds. I
felt the soft breeze wafting over me. I'd walked out of a
black hole.

Chapter Three

All I could do was cry. My head ached with the pressure. 'What now?' I asked.

'You'll be taken to the local police station and put into a cell overnight,' said Mr. Hewitt.

It didn't take long for the police car to reach the local station. I was processed at the front desk then led to a cell. They gave me a hot drink and a meal, then the door well and truly slammed shut behind me.

The loud 'clunk' when it was locked rang in my ears. I looked at the structure pretending to be a bed. The room was small, with a toilet and sink in the corner. *How can I stay here?* I sank onto the bed, next to the tray of food. I curled up as tightly as I could, desperately trying to hold it together. *I need my family. How will I cope without seeing them?*

I couldn't remember a time when I'd felt that worn out, or cried so much. The nausea hadn't left either. I convinced myself to eat something; I needed to keep my strength up. Even after giving birth to my children - naturally believing that would be the hardest thing I would ever have to do in life - I had more energy than I did at that exact moment. *How am I ever going to face Mum and Dad, or my beautiful children?* I rubbed my tired eyes, put some food in my mouth, and tried to concentrate on one thing at a time. The emotional rollercoaster I was on was making me dizzy.

I finished the food, moved the tray onto the floor, and laid on the bed. A thought kept creeping into my head as I lay there, my eyes shut. It was: *'Money is the root of all evil'* - spoken in my father's voice.

I must have dozed off; I couldn't tell for how long, but judging from the noise outside my cell, it was a rowdy Friday night. I could hear shouting and swearing, scuffling sounds, or like someone being pushed along. *A drunk being put away?* From the name-calling, it sounded like a regular visitor to the cells.

The sliding plate in my cell door opened. A pair of eyes peered through, then the clinking of keys and my door was opened by a female police officer. 'I see you've eaten. Try and get some sleep. You've a long journey in the morning. You'll get your breakfast at 6am.'

'What time is it now, please?' I asked. Even though I still had my watch, I wanted to check it was still working.

'It's half-past ten. You might want to sleep as soon as you can. Friday is a busy, noisy night in here.'

I thanked her as she collected the tray and slammed the door shut. I heard keys clink again and the door lock. I put my head on the pillow, and bit down on it firmly so I wouldn't scream.

I tossed and turned, willing myself to sleep. I couldn't get out of my head what Dorothy had told me earlier that day.

She and Ron had been visiting their son, Alex, and family. Alex and I had attended junior school together; he, unlike me, had progressed to the local grammar school and gone on to university, before landing a job as a commercial pilot.

He was happily married, with two boys. Brian, Alex's eldest son, was roughly the same age as my eldest boy, James. Brian had just started his first year at university. Obviously, his family was very proud of him. My own mother constantly held Brian up as an example, in comparison to my family.

As Dorothy had shared her grandson's problems with me on the ferry, it had been clear the situation was destroying her. Despite all Brian had going for him, he was heavily into drugs. He injected heroin frequently, and was a broken skeleton of a man. He'd stolen from his parents and grandparents to feed his addiction, and according to Dorothy, was near death. The family had rallied round, got medical advice, and taken Brian to a top-class retreat in France. Ron and Dorothy stayed nearby in a holiday home.

I knew I'd blushed as she bared her soul. I remembered the sickening feeling of shame under Dorothy's gaze. Naively, I had never – not even once – thought about the evil that drugs bring to families. Or the dismay, mayhem, and severe physical damage they caused.

Am I rotten to the core? I had taken an easy route to make money, with complete disregard for anyone else's welfare. It clearly revealed the true me. *Am I selfish and weak? An amoral monster?* I'd almost contributed to the misery and devastation families had the misfortune to endure. *How was I going to live with this? What had I done? Who am I? A no-good excuse for a human being...*

My body contracted and I jumped up to vomit down the toilet. I crawled back to the bed, tears streaming down my face, my breath putrid, utterly drenched in sweat. I prayed to God to help Brian.

Eventually, my body succumbed to sleep. When I woke, suddenly, I wondered where the hell I was. My heart sank as I remembered. My head thumped from the heavy doors slamming. I shuffled off the bed to the smelly toilet. Then my cell door opened, and a police officer walked in with a tray of food. He didn't look over at me, but I felt ashamed and embarrassed to be sitting on the pot.

He put the tray on the bed. 'You better eat that while it's hot. The meat wagon will be here in an hour to transport you.'

He left as quickly as he'd arrived. *Meat wagon? Transported?* I felt like an old cow. I rinsed my hands as best I could and splashed my face. I knew my eyes had to be swollen, even before I touched my face to check. The tears started again.

I drank some coffee and ate some of the food. I kept coughing, and felt as if I'd be sick at any moment. I paced up and down the tiny space, not sure what to do with myself. I tried to straighten my clothes, so they didn't look like I'd slept in them. When the keys eventually rattled in the door I was still crying.

A woman came in this time; she took handcuffs from her belt and I dutifully put out my arms. She fastened them to my wrists and led me out of the cell. After the relevant paperwork had been done, we walked out of the station.

The pavements looked wet. I'd not heard it rain, and now the sun shone it was quite warm. There wasn't a cloud in the sky; it looked like it would be another sunny August day.

A prison van was parked up, its engine running. I was passed over to another officer and stepped up into the van. It was bleak and oppressive. I walked down a slim aisle, in-between what looked like individual toilet cubicles. I was led into one and the cuffs were taken off. Then I was sat down and strapped in, like some sort of animal. My arms were pushed in front of my body and hung down like a chimp's.

I couldn't move. *God help me.* It struck me that I, a petite size eight, only just fit into the space. *How did a larger person go on?*

What happens if there's an accident? I won't be able to get out. The van started moving. I could only see out of one side. The cubicle doors and walls were some kind of metal. Or wooden...or probably plastic. The only light came from a small window, which, luckily, I faced. I realised that, although I could see out, people could not see in. As the van gained speed, that small window felt like a portal to liberty.

I felt tears fall down my cheeks before they dripped onto my jumper. I couldn't do anything to stop them. I wasn't sobbing, just crying silently, though my breathing was erratic. I had a strange sensation in my chest, as if my heart was breaking, yet still beating.

Houses, industrial buildings, trees, signposts, children, cars and people fleetingly passed by. *They're free...average...just as I'd been. Why had I believed it would be easy?*

'Just pick up the package and drive back. No one will stop you...you're Mrs. Average. Why would anyone suspect you? Think of the money you'll get.' That brief conversation had brought me here. *What hell lies ahead? How I am going to cope with this?* I shut my eyes.

I woke with a start, unsure how long I'd been asleep. I looked out of the window. *How long is this journey going to take?* It felt like hours had passed since I'd been put in the cage. I had pins and needles in one arm. *This is torture.*

The van slowed down. I assumed we were at another police station; we'd stopped a few times to pick up more prisoners en route. Through the window I saw imposing metal gates opening. I only got a side view as we drove through them.

We stopped at a barrier, and I saw a guard waving the van forward. *Oh, Jesus and Mary, I'm inside the gates of Holloway.*

The guard unlocked my cubicle and released the seat straps. I was told to stand. Until then, I'd thought of myself as relatively fit, but every bone in my body felt like a lead weight. I grabbed my handbag off the floor and slung it over my shoulder. The guard roughly put the handcuffs back on my wrists.

I slowly staggered from the van, finding it difficult to hold onto the side with the cuffs on. I felt like an old woman.

I looked round: there were six other women stood in line. We were taken into the large reception area in single file. It was if we'd walked onto a weird film set. There were cameras in every corner of the room, and over all the exits. I wouldn't have noticed them, only one woman in the queue ahead of me suddenly looked up and gestured to the cameras with two fingers.

Guards were everywhere. Big, butch female officers. Their expressions were a mixture of boredom and suspicion. If I was already scared, it dialled up a notch.

A guard shouted above the noise, barking instructions in a cockney accent. I tried to concentrate, as I couldn't understand what she was saying.

I heard many languages spoken around me, but sadly, no friendly Yorkshire accent. I was amongst women of all shapes, sizes and colours. A woman, who I guessed was Nigerian, stared directly at me. She sucked her lips; I was absolutely terrified.

The place had a musty, sweaty smell, interspersed with perfume, shampoo and shoe polish. The level of noise gave me a headache. I kept looking at the other prisoners; one lady cried constantly, like me - others laughed. Some looked as if they were drunk or on drugs. One woman was trying her best to provoke the guards, by shouting obscenities at them.

My name was called out. I stepped forward and was told to enter a side cubicle. Inside, hanging from a peg, was a dirty housecoat. The guard took off my handcuffs and said, 'Arms out. Spread your legs, I'm going to pat you down.' I couldn't believe this was happening again. It didn't make sense. I'd been in a cell all night, driven in a secure van, and handcuffed - what could I possibly have on me?

She finished frisking me, and said, 'Take off your clothes...everything. Put that on.' She pointed to the housecoat.

I panicked. 'I'm on my period, can I keep my knickers on?'

She shook her head. 'Everything off.'

It still didn't sink in. 'I'm not wearing that dirty thing.'

The guard smiled, but without humour. 'It's up to you. Or you can walk around with nothing on.'

She stood, waiting. *This is so demeaning.* She watched while I quickly undressed and put on the smelly, dirty housecoat. I tied a knot in the waist, so that I was completely covered up. I had to put my clothes in what looked like a garbage bag with HMP stamped on it. Then I had to take it over to a different officer who was tasked with searching through our belongings. I was mortified, handing over my bag; my knickers were in there, with a soiled sanitary towel still attached to them.

Whilst my clothes were inspected, I was taken to another guard who was weighing prisoners. I waited in line. When it was my turn, I stepped onto the scales, then I was told to stand at the measuring tape fixed to the wall. The officer brought the stick down heavily on my head.

I was ordered to queue on the other side of the room. As I walked away, the woman after me swore at the officer. 'Are you trying to fucking knock me out?' she shouted as she was measured.

'Watch your language,' said the guard.

'What you going to do about it, screw?'

I felt like a fish out of water. I followed orders obediently, and walked round the prison in a daze. It reminded me of concentration camps I'd seen in documentaries.

I was told to sit opposite a guard at a table. 'Take off all your jewellery, empty your handbag, and fill out this form.'

I identified my possessions, and once the form was complete, they were taken from me, placed into a bag and tagged. 'Can I keep photos of my family with me?'

The reply was short and sharp. 'No.' In a sarcastic tone, the guard added, 'You'll get your possessions back when you leave Holloway.'

I was allocated a number: CF118. It dawned on me that I was no longer a person, but a number. I shuddered, as if someone had walked over my grave.

In the next area, photographs were taken. I felt embarrassed, ashamed and disgusting as the camera captured me walking in line, wearing a dirty housecoat. At a point marked on the floor, I had to turn and face forwards. A flash in my eyes, then back in line. I presumed the photographer was good at his job. If I'd been taking photos that fast, someone's head would have been cut off in the picture. *I hope he does cut my head off.* I certainly never wanted to be reminded of the moment I wore something that looked as if it had never been washed, and being marched through that shit-hole.

Directed to the next queue, I felt a hundred years-old. An irate guard stood outside some toilet cubicles. Doling out sample jars, she snapped at every prisoner, 'Are you dependant on any drugs?' If they said yes, they were directed to the far end of the toilets and a note was made on the jar. If the reply was 'No', the prisoner was herded into the nearer cubicles, all of which had a guard opposite.

I didn't see what difference this question made, as each person peeing into their jar was watched by a guard anyway. I found it difficult to pee whilst being watched. I managed a trickle that was caught in the jar. As I left the cubicle, I noticed a lot of the women just wandered to the next queue; few bothered to wash their hands. I felt even grubbier.

Back in the first cubicle after collecting my 'garbage bag', I was allowed to put my own clothes back on. I happily hung the vile housecoat back on its hook. I came out of the cubicle and looked at the guard for further instructions. *How am I going to get used to being watched constantly?* It was unnerving. I would no longer have any say in what was to happen to me. It was down to strangers, whose job it was to tell me what to do.

The organised chaos seemed endless. I joined another queue and collected my 'provisions': a package of items that someone somewhere had decided were 'essential' when in prison. A blanket, two sheets and a pillow. A small plastic container with a tiny tablet of soap. A tube of toothpaste and a toothbrush. No shampoo or deodorant.

I was given two more plastic containers. One contained small packets of coffee, sugar, powdered milk and tea-bags. The other: a plate, cup, knife, fork and spoon - all made of plastic.

The final queue was for the prison wing to which I'd been assigned. I struggled to carry everything, and I wasn't sure my shaking legs would get me there. I was marched through the dire interior of the high security prison.

I followed the line of prisoners and guards up some steps, still fighting to keep hold of my packages. We walked down a long corridor before stopping at some locked doors. Once inside those, we had to wait until the doors at the opposite end were unlocked. It was claustrophobic, and it gave me an understanding of how animals in zoos went on. We walked down another corridor then turned the corner onto a wing.

On the right-hand side were numerous doors. The guard leading us pointed to me, then the second doorway. I walked into the cell.

Before she took the others to theirs, she said, 'It's 5.30pm now; at 5.55pm you go to the canteen for tea. Take your plate and cutlery with you. Make sure you lock your other things in the locker when leaving your cell, or your stuff will get nicked.'

I nodded and they all moved off. I took in my surroundings. The room was long but narrow, and painted an off-white colour. There were two single beds against opposite walls. Next to each bed was a small cabinet or locker that consisted of a shelf, two tiny drawers and a small cupboard. Each cabinet had a key in the lock. Both beds were unmade, which led me to think I wouldn't be the only one allocated to this cell.

I put my stuff onto one of the beds. At the far end of the cell, on the back wall, there was a window. I tried to open it, but it only moved about four inches - just enough to squeeze my hand through. I put my face up to the glass and felt a slight breeze against my skin. It seemed like years since I'd breathed fresh air.

Also in the cell was a small sink, and above it, a plastic mirror screwed to the wall. Off to one side was a small toilet cubicle. I noticed a red button on one wall, which was clearly some sort of alarm; I was later told it was so the guards could be called in an emergency if the cells were in 'lock down'.

Exhausted, I sat on the bed in a daze, not quite sure what to do. *Should I make up a bed; if so, which one? On which side of the room do I want to sleep? Will I even sleep?* I was amazed that tears still ran down my face. *Where did all the liquid come from? Will it ever stop?*

Chapter Four

Someone passed the cell door and looked in. 'If I were you, I'd get a move on, or you'll miss tea.' I hurriedly put the bundles into one of the lockers, taking out the plastic bags I needed and locking the rest away. I put the key in my pocket and practically ran after the woman who'd just spoken to me. I followed her round corners, down some steps, certain I was going the right way, as other women were walking in the same direction. I wiped the tears from my cheeks.

Entering the canteen, the noise was simply unbearable. Women chattered amongst loud laughter, shouting and swearing. The clattering of plates on tables, chairs scraping the floor when people sat down; people moving about quickly, holding their plates, cups, knives and forks, shouting at others to move out of their way. There was lots of pushing and shoving in the queue for food.

Guards were everywhere, watching, their chains jangling with keys and handcuffs. I joined the queue quickly, unpacking my plate and cup. I didn't have a clue what I was meant to do – I just watched everyone else. I tucked the plastic bags under my armpit, and at the food hatch, I held out my plate. Food was slopped onto it, and I was nudged to keep the line moving. I opted for bangers and mash, not that there was much choice; it was either sausage or the vegetarian option.

I held my plate out in front of me. 'Thank you,' I said to each person handing out the meat or veg, smiling at each of them as they served me. They all replied 'Thank you', but in a disparaging way. I was alarmed; I'd been brought up to be polite.

The women frightened me. Though they all smiled at me, it was creepy. It dawned on me...they obviously knew I was a new prisoner. *Were they trying to intimidate me? There I go again, being paranoid...* It was as if I'd landed on another planet.

When served, I walked slowly towards the tables, not sure where to sit. I'd seen the films; sit in the wrong place and you get your neck stabbed. *Whoa, where did that come from?* I tried to calm myself. The lady I'd followed into the canteen waved me over to a table at the side of the room, near to where some guards were stood. Gratefully, I sat opposite her, and felt safety in the fact the guards were so close.

'You new here? First time, huh?' She stuffed some food in her mouth.

'Yes. Is it that obvious? I'm Tilly...I arrived this afternoon.' Unsure of protocol, or what to say next, I fiddled with the plastic container that held my cutlery. She carried on talking in-between chewing. I could clearly see the food in her mouth; I thought I was going to be sick.

'My advice: keep your head down. Don't cause trouble, do your time, keep off the drugs.' I just nodded and unpacked my knife and fork, setting them on the table. I didn't know if I'd even be able to eat.

She chattered on. 'I'd eat all the food you get, because you don't get much in here.' I smiled and reluctantly tucked into the food.

We just sat there eating for a few minutes. 'Do we get a drink with our meal?' I asked.

She laughed and pointed to a boiler at the side of the serving hatch. 'That screw next to the boiler will show you.' I thanked her and took a few more mouthfuls, but knew I wouldn't clear my plate - my stomach was too unsettled.

I got up and started to walk away. 'Take your things with you,' the woman said. I collected all my items from the table and went over to the boiler. The guard nodded, which I assumed was permission to pour the water. I stuffed what I could under my arm again.

When my cup was full, I walked back to the same table. It was difficult to carry everything and not spill the water at the same time. *Why don't they give you a bag or tray to carry all this around?* I ripped open sachets of coffee and powdered milk from my container and watched them dissolve in the hot water. Stirring the liquid with my plastic spoon, I sorrowfully realised that, for the foreseeable future, I'd be drinking out of plastic cups, instead of the lovely china I used at home.

Whilst sipping the coffee, surreptitiously, I looked around the room. I tried to burn some understanding in my mind of the canteen's layout and how it all worked. I noticed a big clock over the door. The room was at full capacity; women of all ages, nationalities, colours and sizes seemed quite at home. They appeared content to eat and chat with those sat with them, as if they were dining out with friends. The manic rush for food was now over, yet the atmosphere still seemed charged to me.

I desperately tried not to stare at anyone directly, and hoped I blended in. The last thing I wanted to do was offend someone. The whole thing was surreal. It was like being back at junior school, sussing out who was going to be friendly, who the bullies might be. *Will I survive this?*

The clock showed 6.45pm, the date underneath was Saturday 30th August 1997. My only companion at that point noticed me looking at the clock. 'When you're doing time, you'll get used to doing time,' she said.

'I don't understand,' I replied.

She shrugged. 'You will, love, you will.' She then pointed to a table near the exit. A guard was sat there and a queue started to form. 'That's where you get stuff. You have to pay, once a week. You should join the queue...you get a phone card. Lucky for you, the first one is free. Get yours on the way out, you might as well get what you're due.' She started picking her teeth.

'Where do I put the food from my plate?' I asked. 'I can't eat any more.' She pointed to a bin near the serving hatch. 'Thank you for helping me,' I said. 'It's much appreciated.' She just nodded.

I collected everything, scraped my leftover food into the bin, put the stuff back into my containers, and joined the queue. The queue moved slowly and I found it tiring. *How will time pass quickly, if I've to queue for everything?*

When it was my turn, the guard looked up. 'I don't know you. What's your number?' I replied with my number and name. 'Ah, yes, this is your first day. You get a phone card, free. Any subsequent ones will be paid for. You can use the telephones near your wing. Lock-up is at 8pm. Tomorrow, you'll have an induction after breakfast.'

She then wrote some notes and handed me a phone card. I half expected her to say, 'Enjoy your stay!'

Quietly, I said, 'I'm on my period and don't have any more sanitary towels. Where can I get some from?'

She leaned forward. 'Go to the medical hatch just before lock-up. They'll take care of you.'

As she'd seemed approachable, I said, 'Where are the telephones again, and the medical hatch?'

She glared at me. 'You can't get lost in here, love. You'll find them before lock-up.'

Squirming, I muttered, 'Thank you.'

As I walked away I wondered how I was supposed to know when lock-up was. I no longer had a watch in my possession. I remembered the big clock over the canteen doorway. It said 7pm. I had an hour.

I wandered down a corridor then turned a corner, trying to get my bearings. Ahead of me were two male guards chatting away. Until then, I'd only come across female staff, which I naturally assumed would be the case in a women's prison. I'd never consider myself a prude, but I shuddered at the thought. *When we'd undressed earlier, was a male guard watching? That's just wrong. But what rights do I have now?* I tried to think of something else. I passed them feeling slightly embarrassed, as if they could hear my thoughts.

I followed a few women around another corner and saw a guard. *I must be near the telephones.* What a surprise...queues at each one. I got in line behind three women, one already talking on the phone. I patiently waited, trying not to look like I was listening in to their conversations. The time passed slowly and I wrestled with myself over who to ring first: my children or Jake.

After what seemed like years, my turn came. I placed my plastic containers between my legs, inserted the phone card, picked up the receiver, and rang home.

Jake picked up. He sounded tired. 'Hi Jake,' I said.

'Hi. Are you alright?'

'Not really. It's like I'm in a nightmare, waiting to wake up. I'm tired and feel grubby. I'd crawl over hot coals and broken glass to be home with you now.'

After a few seconds of silence, he said, 'I'd love you to be home now. What a mess.' He cleared his throat. 'I've been ringing your parents and the kids. They're upset. I've told Elliot you've been caught speeding and won't be home for a while. I didn't know what to say to him.' His voice began to break, and for a moment I thought he was crying. 'I'll put him on, he wants to talk to you.'

Before I could say no, I heard him shout Elliot. Then thunderous footsteps; I imagined my boy running down the stairs to get to the phone. My eyes stung. I fought to keep control, but I was shaking.

'Hello, Mum. You've been naughty! How fast were you going? When will you be home? Dad made tea. It was awful.' I started laughing through my tears. 'Are you there, Mum?'

I hurriedly cleared my throat. 'It's lovely to hear your voice, Elliot. What did you have for tea? Have you walked the dog and fed her?'

'We had burnt fish fingers with baked beans. But Grandma is making roast beef tomorrow, so I can't wait. I walked Ellie. She had a good run, but it was too hot. She ate her food and now she's asleep in her bed. Dad's getting a video to watch tonight. Will you be home on Monday?'

He sounded so...normal. 'I hope to see you soon. You enjoy your film. Don't go to bed too late, and be good while I'm not there. Do your share of the jobs. And please be good tomorrow for Grandma. Now put your dad back on, please.' As he handed the phone back to Jake, I had to bite my hand to stop myself from sobbing.

'Tilly, all the family are getting together tomorrow over lunch, to sort out who'll be able to visit.'

I had to take a few deep breaths before I could reply. 'Okay. I'll ring tomorrow, if I have enough money on this card.' I steadied myself with my hand against the wall; I felt like I was about to faint. 'I love you,' I whispered.

Jake paused for a few seconds, before saying, 'I love you, too.'

I wanted to ask why he'd hesitated, but instead, I just said, 'I'll ring you tomorrow. Night.' I placed the receiver in its cradle, and was nearly knocked over by the woman in the queue behind me. I lost my grip and the containers crashed to the ground.

She snarled, 'Out the way. I need to talk to my family before lock-up.' I moved quickly, not daring to reply, and picked up my things.

Halfway down the corridor, I had to stand against the wall for a few minutes, just to muster the strength to move on. I felt as if I was submerged in treacle, walking against a heavy force, moving in slow motion. It took all my physical and emotional strength to carry on. I was aware that there were people all around me, but I didn't want to talk to anyone or ask which direction I needed.

I just walked. I turned a few corners and started following some women who'd said they were going to collect their meds. Shortly, we came to the medical point, and another queue. The women stood in line and shuffled up to the hatch. When it was their turn, they leant forward, and after a short conversation, a hand would appear from the hatch to deposit something into their open mouths. The recipient would then give an exaggerated swallow before shuffling off. Eventually, I reached the hatch. I explained I needed sanitary towels, gave my prison number, collected the items, then moved off to my wing.

Not quite sure how I got there, I found myself in my cell. Just as I was about to sit on one of the beds a guard put their head in the doorway. 'You might want to make your bed up first, before you rest. Lock-up in five minutes. Get your cup ready at the hatch if you want a hot drink...it'll be your last until breakfast.'

I managed to smile and say, 'Thank you.' She started whistling and turned to walk away. I ran to the door. 'Am I in here on my own?'

'For tonight, yes.' She started to whistle again. The

tune faded as she moved along. A sense of loss came over me, and I felt completely alone.

I rinsed out my plastic cup and waited on the bed. I had a feeling I wouldn't sleep, even though I was utterly exhausted. The banging of cell doors resonated through my cell - it made my stomach turn. I started to recite the Lord's Prayer, something I'd not done in years.

At that point, some of the prisoners started to bang on their doors. There was a chorus of shouts, and I even heard someone howl like a wolf. *Am I in a jail or a zoo?* Tears flowed again. My eyes were so sore, and my mouth unbearably dry. I blew my nose on the horrible toilet paper, desperately trying to block out the peculiar sounds.

I heard footsteps approaching. The hatch slid open and a male guard said, 'Your cup for hot water.'

I put down my cup as steadily as I could manage and he filled it. 'Thank you,' I said, but he just shut the hatch. I got my sachets from the cabinet and made a coffee.

After I'd finished it, I got out my bedding and began to make up the bed nearest the door. It felt strangely relaxing to do something normal and mundane for a few minutes; it gave my brain a short rest and I felt a little calmer. The bed made, I picked up the small towel I'd found amongst the bedding. The delight at finding the towel was immense. The last shower I'd had was on Thursday morning and it was now Saturday night. I couldn't remember a time in my life when I'd not showered for so long. I felt so filthy, that I tried to have a strip wash at the tiny sink. I kept refilling the bowl up and letting out the dirty water until every bit of my body had been thoroughly washed. I began to feel more human. It was remarkable what a tiny tablet of soap could cover.

I pictured my bathroom at home, with all its shampoos, conditioners, moisturisers, luxury soaps, deodorants and perfumes. How my life had changed.

Wearily, I put my dirty knickers back on, thankful that I'd least been able to wear a clean sanitary towel. I got under the sheets, curled up tightly, and shut my eyes.

Chapter Five

The noises kept me on edge throughout the night. I was petrified. *Will I get to the stage where I howl like a wolf? Please, God, don't let me go mad.* I held myself tightly, aware that I was rocking backwards and forwards. I needed to sleep. I felt so wretched, but somehow, I needed to block out all the noise.

My mind started to wander, and I thought about my life. The breakup of my marriage, the divorce settlement, and getting together with Jake. We'd put a deposit on our house after I sold my hairdressing salon. Jake had started a small scrap metal business; I helped him with the paperwork and some customer visits, in-between mobile hairdressing appointments.

We had a mortgage, like everyone else I knew. We both worked hard, and I certainly thought we'd made a good, solid start to our life together. Jake didn't have any children when we met, though he got on well with my two. He was absolutely over the moon when I gave birth to his son, Elliot, seven years ago.

I'd certainly felt that life was good. We holidayed abroad, we both had good cars, though one was bought with a loan. Like most couples, we dined out every now and again, went to the pictures or theatre a few times a year. Business was steady for both of us. I'd loved my life. Until a year ago.

I'd noticed a change in Jake. Nothing specific, but occasionally, he seemed a different person. He could be quite moody at times; when I tried to talk to him he'd just clam up, saying there was nothing wrong. Around this time, he started mixing with people I didn't know. He told me he'd met them through a friend of a friend.

He went on golfing days with this new circle of friends, to conferences, and on a few nights out. He'd sometimes drop a name in conversation, but if I asked questions, he'd change the subject. 'You'll meet them soon,' he said. They'd invited us to a few events over the coming summer: the races, a few functions, and even a day out on a yacht.

I found out why Jake had been so cagey by accident. Several months before, I'd answered the phone and learned that Jake had missed a couple of our mortgage payments. When I confronted him, he said he was waiting for some money owed to him, that he'd sort it and I wasn't to worry. There was something about his manner that made me hunt down our bank statements the next day when he was out; something just felt off.

I remember being stunned, frozen to the spot, as I drank in what the statements told me. Lump sum withdrawals: £1000 here and there, in cash.

He's having an affair! I could feel my cheeks burning. I tried to remain rational. *When he comes home, we need to have 'the talk'.*

That night, Jake was out with 'the boys'. Usually, he came home around 11.30pm. I'd put Elliot to bed after we watched television together; I couldn't concentrate on the film - I was fidgety and irate. I cleared away the supper dishes, did some ironing...anything to keep my mind from putting two and two together. I checked on Elliot at 10pm; he was asleep.

I changed into my nightdress and laid on the bed for a while, gathering my thoughts. Then I went back downstairs and paced around, waiting for, yet dreading, Jake's arrival. I eventually sat in the kitchen, sifting through the bank statements.

Jake came home at 1.30am, slightly drunk, and not in a good mood. I made some coffee. He sat at the kitchen table and noticed the bank statements. He gave me a sheepish look.

'Are you having an affair?' I said.

He looked at me, horrified. 'I've never even looked at another woman! How can you say that? I'm happy with you. With our life.'

I started to get annoyed. *Classic answer.* I pressed on. 'What about the money, Jake?' At that he broke down.

He told me he'd been gambling for a while. He'd lost large amounts of money playing poker at the casino with his new friends. He also admitted to taking cocaine occasionally. That explained a lot.

He said he knew he was in trouble; he'd tried to recoup the money so he didn't have to tell me. 'I didn't want to worry you,' he said.

I was horrified...I'd not imagined things were this messed up. Though I was relieved he wasn't having an affair, I was naturally concerned about him taking cocaine.

We talked through the night, and I got an idea of how much he owed. 'I'll talk to the bank, see if we can work out a plan to pay the mortgage arrears,' I said. I was hopeful we could pull our belts in. 'We can just do without for a time, until we get back on our feet.'

Jake agreed to everything I said, and he seemed sincere. 'Whatever it takes to get things back on track.' I was just glad we'd not argued and, instead, reconnected.

'You've got to stop gambling and taking drugs,' I told him. 'And you can't keep secrets from me again.' He nodded slowly.

The next month, I checked the bank statement. A payment had been made on the mortgage, though we were still in arrears. I worked extra hours, and shopped for cheaper food items. We cut out treats such as takeaways, bought drinks to have in the house, and banned nights out - and anything else that cost money. I still hired a video each Saturday night, for Elliot more than anything.

There was just one night out, a few months after our head-to-head in the kitchen. It was Jake's birthday and I wanted to have some sort of celebration after months of scraping by. I planned to get a couple of bottles of wine and cook his favourite meal at home.

'But we've been invited out, to a restaurant,' he said when I brought it up. 'My mate Tony's treat.'

'Jake, we can't afford to go out.'

'It'll only be the cost of a taxi and a few drinks. Come on...it's for my birthday.'

I sighed. We hadn't been out for months, and it was my chance to meet these new friends of his. He'd already persuaded my mum to have Elliot for the night, so I relented. It was his birthday, after all.

The following Saturday morning, I received a phone call from Jackie, Tony's wife. She gave me directions to the restaurant, and told me what time we should be there.

We got a taxi to the restaurant. As we walked in, I saw three couples stood by the bar. Jake introduced me to Jackie and we had a good chat; it was reassuring to finally meet her. I'd half-suspected she was the one Jake was having an affair with, a feeling that only strengthened when she'd rung the house. Now she was in-front of me, I could see she wasn't his type.

She was older than me, and when she stood next to her husband, it was clear to anyone she was besotted. I began to relax.

During the meal, I was introduced to the other couples. One lady had also been a hairdresser before she got married, so we had that in common. The meal was beautiful and everyone was chatting; it was a really good mix, and I found I was enjoying myself.

After we'd eaten - all a little merry from the wine

we'd consumed – Tony invited everyone back to their house for drinks.

'Should we be going?' I whispered to Jake. 'It means paying for a taxi to and from their house.'

He just laughed. 'Stop being a spoilsport. We can afford a couple of taxis.' I was still a bit worried, but reasoned it was his birthday. We shared a taxi there with Tony and Jackie.

The cab pulled up at some tall wrought-iron gates. Tony opened them with a remote device from his pocket. The driveway was long, ending in a circular gravelled area in front of the house.

The house was enormous. We entered through a large wooden door, into an expansive hallway. It was like something out of a magazine - tasteful, not flashy. Tony said he'd get some drinks and everyone headed into a large living room.

'Jackie, where's the toilet?' I said.

'Follow me.' She led me down a hallway. I was in awe; I'd not seen a bathroom like it before. Hanging from the high ceiling was a glittering chandelier. Huge mirrors adorned the walls and gleaming tiles sparkled. *Her downstairs loo's bigger than our whole bathroom! I bet she has a cleaner; I wouldn't like to have to keep this room clean.* As she used the toilet we chatted. I wondered how much money they had...I imagined the upkeep on that house was huge.

I used the loo, washed my hands, and started to re-apply my lipstick. At that point, Jackie took a little parcel of powder from her handbag. 'Fancy snorting some stuff?'

I refused as politely as I could, trying not to show how shocked I was.

She laughed. 'It helps me feel alive.'

I excused myself and left her to it. I was sobering up quickly. *I bet this is where Jake gets his cocaine from.* I walked into the living room. Music was playing and drinks were lined up on the long coffee table. The other two ladies were sat on a sofa, chatting.

'Where have the men gone?' I asked.

'Oh, they're starting a game of poker in the dining room,' one replied.

I took a drink and sat down, trying to mask how I felt. I joined in with the conversation now and again, but inside I was livid. *Jake shouldn't be gambling!* I wanted to scream at him, and I longed to go home, but I had no other choice than waiting for them to finish whilst trying to control my anger.

Jackie came back in, singing along to music that was playing. 'Come on, have a dance!' She was high as a kite. The other two women got up and started to jig around.

I was too angry to dance. *God, Jake, what are you doing?* I kept sipping at my drink; I wasn't having a good time at all. But I didn't want to show myself up, or embarrass Jake by making a scene. *I don't know these people that well...what would it matter?*

I was just about to jump up and go into the dining room when Jake came in. I could tell he was high, too. *That's all I need.* He walked over to me and sat down. He tried to put his arm round me and leant in for a kiss. I felt like slapping his face, but instead, I just shoved him away.

'Tilly, don't be mourngy! It's my birthday.' He kept repeating, 'I've been a good boy, I haven't played poker tonight.' He started laughing and wanted a cuddle.

'We're going home...now,' I said, through gritted teeth. 'Jackie, can I use your phone to ring a taxi?'

Tony walked in at that moment. 'I'll ring a taxi for you,' he said. I watched Jake grab another drink.

I had to get some fresh air, I was absolutely fuming. I stood near the front door and smoked a cigarette.

A couple of minutes later, Tony came outside. 'The taxi will be ten minutes,' he said. He started to chat. I wasn't really listening until he said, 'Is everything okay, Tilly? You look sad.'

I don't know what made me confide in a stranger... maybe the drink loosened my tongue, or perhaps I was so mad with Jake I couldn't think straight. 'Jake's using money we don't have. We're getting into...financial difficulties.' I regretted saying it as soon as the words were out. 'Take no notice of me. I'm tired and I've drunk too much. We should go home.'

Luckily, the headlights of the taxi could be seen shining through the gate. Tony pressed his device and the car drove up to the house. We bundled Jake inside; he was a bit floppy, as if his legs had stopped working. I thanked Jackie and Tony for the night out, and said goodbye to everyone. I sat next to Jake on the back seat. His eyes were closed and his head rested on my lap.

Just before we drove off, Tony shoved a card in my hand. 'Give me a ring, I might be able to help out. Don't worry.' As the taxi pulled away from the house, and the gates started to shut behind us, I looked back. Tony was still stood at the door, staring down the driveway.

On the way home, Jake kept saying how much he loved me. 'I haven't gambled tonight. I've been a good boy,' he drawled. I just let him ramble on. I didn't reply in case I lost my temper. To be honest, I was disgusted with him. But more so with myself, telling a stranger about my problems. *What did Tony mean, that he'd able to help?* I paid the taxi driver and pushed Jake into the house, where I had to stop myself from punching him.

Jake kept saying he wanted to make love to me. I made it clear that was not going to happen. I was too tired to argue; I really didn't want a fight. I let the dog out and stood at the patio doors waiting for her to come back in, smoking a cigarette.

'You can stay downstairs and sleep on the sofa,' I snapped, 'I'm going to bed.' He refused at first, saying he wanted to be next to me. I made it plain - either he slept on the sofa, or I would.

He obviously couldn't sleep, as he kept playing music. At one point, I had to get up and tell him to turn the volume down, as it was so late. 'You've spoilt my night,' he said. 'It's not fair, it's my birthday.' I struggled to stay silent and went back upstairs.

****

I woke suddenly to banging noises. My heart raced. 'Jake? What's going on?' Startled, I looked around, then slowly my mind took it in. *I'm not at home, Jake's not here.* The banging carried on, so I got out of bed, used the toilet, washed and dressed - yet again - into my grubby, and now seriously creased, clothing. I knew I'd slept, but for how long, I wasn't sure. I still felt drained, like death warmed up.

My cell door was unlocked and the male guard said, 'Princess Diana's dead!' I walked to the open door, just staring at him. He continued down the corridor, opening each cell door, saying the same thing. *Is this some kind of sick joke?* I quickly went back in my cell and took out my cutlery and powdered drinks. *Should I make my bed or leave it? Do I lock away my bedding? Bugger it, I better get to breakfast and find out what's going on...*

As I walked to the canteen I heard snippets from other prisoners about a car crash. Someone said it happened in Paris. The queue in the canteen seemed longer than the previous day. I got in line and a woman behind me started chatting. Everyone was talking nineteen to the dozen; it sounded like a cattle market.

It took all my concentration to hear what she said. 'What do you think about Princess Diana? They say she was still alive when the ambulance arrived.'

I shook my head slowly. 'I can't believe it. Bloody hell, it's awful for her boys.'

The whole place brimmed with a nervous energy. Some women were crying. I felt for a lot of mothers in there who were most likely thinking of their children, as I was.

After I'd been given my food, I spotted a table with only one woman sat at it, so I headed that way. She nodded as I sat down; she looked heartbroken. 'Bad news travels fast in here,' she muttered.

I nodded. 'I can't believe it. What a tragedy.'

The woman who'd been behind me in the queue sat next to me. As she organised her plate and things on the table, she said, 'She was so beautiful. What a way to die.'

I tried to eat, to keep up my strength. *You never know what's going to happen in life.* I snapped back to reality when the woman asked, 'How long have you been in here?'

'I came in yesterday.' I sounded pathetic.

'Me too,' she admitted. 'It's my first time and I'm scared shitless. I didn't sleep a wink...all the noise! I can't stop crying.'

'I know exactly how you feel.'

The lady opposite us looked bored. She tried to bring the conversation back to Diana. 'The royal family have had it now. People only put up with them because they all loved Diana.' I nodded, but didn't reply.

A guard walked over to the table. She asked my name and that of the woman sat next to me. 'After your breakfast, queue up by the exit. You'll be taken to the induction room.'

There looked to be around ten other prisoners in

the line for induction. In single file, with a guard at the front and one behind us, we walked through numerous security gates to a room with large windows. Sunshine streamed in. Desks and chairs were arranged like in a classroom. At the front of the room was a whiteboard, and a few posters were hung on the walls.

It was a cheery enough room, yet everyone looked sad and gloomy. One woman asked about Diana. 'After this induction, you'll be able to go to the television room and watch the news,' said the guard. 'The whole country is in shock.'

A few more guards walked in; one demanded that we be quiet. An older, chubby guard, with greying hair and the soft manner of someone's grandmother, asked that we sit down. We obeyed, and she started explaining daily procedures. She gave times of lock-up, and told us how much time we'd spend working or studying. I didn't pay much attention - I just wanted to go home.

My ears pricked up when she said we'd have to visit the doctor. A few prisoners stood up and I followed suit. The girl next to me asked, 'What are you going to do - work or education?'

'Work, I think.' I was brusque with her, but more annoyed with myself that I'd not listened to the information.

Unsurprisingly, queues started to form. The girl pointed to one of the queues and said, 'That one looks the smallest.' She took my arm and led me over.

'Where are you from?' I said.

'From Wrenthorpe in Yorkshire. Do you know it?'

I laughed. 'I do! I'm from Normanton. I'm Tilly.'

She smiled. 'Mia.'

We chatted, trying to find out if either of us knew anyone in common. We forgot our surroundings, and compared notes on familiar landmarks. I was so happy to talk to someone from my neck of the woods, and someone who was also experiencing their first full day in Holloway.

We eventually reached the front of the queue and both said we wanted to work. We were assigned a personal officer, whose name was Miss Woods, then we were told to see the doctor straightaway. After lunch we had to report to Miss Woods, who would organise work from Monday.

A guard said, 'Do you want to attend church? There are services every Sunday. Obviously, you're too late for the service today.'

'I'm not that religious,' said Mia, 'but I think I'll go to service next week.'

I agreed. 'I'll go to church, too, and pray to get out of here.'

We followed a guard who took us to the doctor. 'Do you think the doctor will give me something to help me sleep?' said Mia.

'I don't know...I guess we'll find out soon enough. Last night there were queues of women getting tablets.'

The corridors weaved all over the place, but soon we were at the hatch I'd visited the previous evening, which wasn't far from my cell. 'This is the medical wing,' the guard said over his shoulder. 'Over there is the medical hatch. You collect your meds from there, usually, just before lock-up.'

'My cell is up there,' I said, pointing upwards.

'Above the medical wing?' said the guard.

'Yes.'

'You might stay there until you get a court date, or you might be moved to another cell. It depends.' The guard couldn't have looked less interested.

Mia went in to the doctor first. Whilst I waited, my

mind was consumed with thoughts of my lovely children: James, Kate and Elliot. Then I thought of my mother and father. I had to bite my lip to stop myself crying.

When Mia came out she gave me a thumbs up. 'I'll wait here for you.'

The doctor, who looked as tired as I felt, was tall and skinny, with pale skin. He asked some questions about my general health...was I drug dependant, my medical history, heart problems, diabetes, etc. He took my blood pressure and listened to my heart. He then asked me to sit on the edge of the examination bed before tapping my knee bone with a small hammer.

'Touch your toes. Shut your eyes and put a finger on your nose.' *This is a more thorough examination than I get at my own doctors!* He handed me a plastic jar and pointed to a toilet door at the end of the room. 'Can you fill this sample jar, please?' I headed to the loo and did as he asked.

I handed him the sample. 'Are you anxious?' he asked.

I started to sob. 'I can't believe I'm in here. I know I've committed a crime, but I don't think I'll survive in prison.'

He nodded. 'I'll write you a prescription. The pills will help you sleep. Pick them up at the medical hatch tonight.' He shouted the next prisoner number on his list and I left the room.

'Hurry up! We can get to the TV room and hear more about Diana before lunch,' said Mia excitedly. I followed her, though I wasn't really bothered about seeing the news. I had enough on my mind. It was sad that Diana was dead, but I was in pain and I wanted to go home, to get my life back.

We reached the TV room. There was only room to stand. Loads of women were glued to the programme.

Some were crying while others joked around. I turned to Mia. 'I'm going to make a phone call before lunch. I'll see you in the canteen.' She moved into the crowd to get a better view of the television.

As I approached the telephone area I saw a few prisoners already queuing, some looking anxious. I got in line and fidgeted with the phone card I'd been given, hoping there was enough money left on it to call my kids as well as Jake. *Are they watching the news about Diana?*

I dialled my ex-husband's number, hoping against hope that he wouldn't answer, and just praying Kate or James would be there. It rang for ages and I panicked that they were all out. Eventually, my ex, John, picked up. 'Hello John, it's Tilly.'

For a moment, there was only silence. I even thought he'd put the phone down. 'Hi,' he said quietly. 'How are you?'

'I don't know what to say,' I stuttered. 'I know I've been an idiot. I'm in a real mess. Is Kate or James there? I really need to speak to them.'

'I'm sorry you're in this situation. If I can help in any way, let me know. Kate's here...I'll get her, just a minute.'

'Thank you,' I said softly. I heard voices then muffled sounds, as if John had put the receiver under his armpit - a habit I saw him do countless times when we were married.

'Mum? Oh, Mum, are you alright?' Kate's voice was so full of concern and I could tell she was crying, which set me off, too.

'Kate, I'm so sorry. So very sorry. I hope you can forgive me.' I wiped my eyes as best I could on my sleeve.

'How are you getting on? I just can't believe all this. I never thought you'd do anything like that.'

I started to sob. 'I know, I've ruined everything. I

love you, you know that? I wish I could turn back time but what's done is done. I need to see you...will you come and visit? I know I've messed up big time. I just need to see you and the boys. That will help me get through, whatever happens.'

'We're all here for you, Mum. Don't give up, whatever you do. We'll get through this, I promise.' She paused to blow her nose. 'I'm coming to see you on Saturday. Elliot's coming too. We'll get a train. James will come soon after. What do you need that I can bring with me?'

I managed a smile. My ever-practical daughter, who was so grown up for her seventeen years. I started to feel less alone. 'You're so good, Kate, God bless you. I need some underwear, deodorant...some t-shirts and jeans. Perhaps another jumper...whatever you think, really. Thank you so much. I can't wait to see you.'

We chatted for a few more minutes, about her work, her friends...normal stuff that kept us from becoming emotional. She said James was out; I'd need to ring him another time.

After we said our goodbyes, I felt stronger - for a moment at least.

Chapter Six

I reached the canteen, which, funnily enough, was the place where I felt most at ease: the caterpillar queues, the noise, the familiar hubbub, the smells...I didn't feel as scared there as I did throughout the rest of the prison.

Mia was already at a table but when she spotted me she came over and we joined the queue. We got our food, and found another table. She chatted as we ate, telling me all about the news reports on Diana. I noticed, for the first time, that I'd eaten everything and thoroughly enjoyed it. *I must've been hungry.* I wondered if that was the case, or if it was down to being with Mia, a fellow Yorkshire lass. In my heart, I knew it was because my family were going to visit soon. That thought uplifted me more than anything.

After lunch, we met our personal officer, Miss Woods. As we entered the room, she stood up. 'Take a seat over there.' She pointed to seats lined up against the opposite wall.

A couple of women were already sat there. 'I'll be with you shortly,' called Miss Woods.

I heard one of the other women mutter, 'She told us that half an hour ago. Looks a bit dizzy to me.'

Miss Woods did indeed look harassed. On her desk sat piles of paperwork. She smiled to the prisoner sat across from her and carried on. She looked in her late thirties, had short blonde hair, and was of medium build and height. She leafed through the pile of paperwork and some fell to the floor. The prisoner she was dealing with jumped up and helped put the papers back on the desk. Miss Woods reminded me of a teacher who'd taught Elliot. That made me think. *I don't know how long I'm going to be in here. How much will I see Elliot? Will I miss him growing up?*

Mia glanced at me. 'Tilly? Are you ill? You've gone pale.'

'It's okay. I'll be fine in a minute.' Inside, I was dying.

Miss Woods tried her best to help during that first meeting. She seemed pleasant enough and was certainly informative. She kept saying, 'I'm here to help. If you need anything, let me know.' She spoke quickly, with a soft Irish lilt. I could understand her, which was a start. She arranged work for Mia and me, starting the next day. Our wage would be £2.50 per day.

She made the job sound easy, and I looked forward to it. A chance to think about something else, to do something autonomous. By the time we finished the induction it had gone 4pm. I was ready for a rest – things were starting to get on top of me.

I learned that we were locked in our cells every day between 4pm and 6pm. Dinner was at 6pm, lock-up was 8pm to 8am. Every day started the same: the bang on your cell door at 7am. Your cell opened at 8am, ready for breakfast. Work or education ran from 9am until 11am. We then had half-an-hour outdoor exercise until 11.30am. Lunch was 11.30am to 12.30pm, lock-up 12.30pm to 2pm. Work or education from 2pm until 4pm. Then we had to do it all again the next day.

Back in my cell, I laid on the bed - my thoughts a mixture of hope and despair. *Soon, I'll see my family. I just need to get through this next week, and that'll be my reward...seeing the ones I love.* A bonus was the change of clothing Kate promised to bring. I thought about starting work the following day; hopefully, it would keep my mind occupied, and if I earned some money I'd be able to buy the essentials: cigarettes, phone cards, toiletries. I tried to have a nap before dinner...if only I could have blocked out the noise. On the outside, I'd never really appreciated the luxury of peace and quiet, but I longed for it at that moment.

I managed to doze off eventually and felt groggy when I woke. *I need to get some decent sleep.* The emotions I was experiencing, how my mind jumped from one thing to another...it was exhausting. I splashed some water on my face and stared at my reflection in the plastic mirror that warped my face into a weird shape. *Don't cry*, I told myself. *Keep strong. You've nearly got through today - another day down. Keep positive.* I hurriedly collected my things to take to the canteen when my cell door was unlocked. *After tea, I'll ring Jake and Elliot. Find out how Mum and Dad are.* I felt ashamed that I couldn't summon up the courage to ring them myself.

Dinner was a plate of salad with two slices of ham, and a slice of bread and butter. Dessert was an orange. I ate it all again, thankful my appetite seemed to be getting back to normal. *It's the only way I'll stay strong and healthy.* Getting water for my coffee was certainly easier; Mia stayed at the table with all our stuff so I could just concentrate on carrying the two plastic cups of hot water without worrying about any of my things being pinched. It would make things easier in here...a friend, or at least someone I could trust. It would make day-to-day life in prison more tolerable. I really hoped Mia would be that friend.

We made our drinks and chatted for a while, then I jumped up. 'I'm going to phone Jake then collect my meds.'

'Me too,' she said. 'I need to ring home as well. I hope the meds work and knock me out.' She looked sad for a moment. 'If I don't sleep soon, I'm going to go mad.'

'It's new to us, and terrifying....hopefully, in a week, we'll be more used to it. Things can only get better.'

She shrugged her shoulders and stared into her coffee. I knew she'd heard me, even if she didn't believe what I'd said.

As Mia and I made our way to the telephones, we talked about our partners. She'd been in love with hers for a few years, but he was a ladies' man; he'd cheated on her and broken her heart. She'd split up with him six months previous, but they were in the process of getting back together.

'I've been with Jake for eight years,' I told her. 'Everything had been good until a year ago.' I became angry as I explained Jake's behaviour.

When it was my turn on the phones, I wasn't even sure if I wanted to talk to Jake. But I knew I wanted to speak to Elliot. I picked up the receiver, which was still warm from the woman who'd just used it. I rang the number and waited. It rang and rang. I redialled, assuming I'd rung the wrong number. *Elliot should be home by now. And where's Jake?* Still no answer.

I hung up and was about to redial when a woman behind me said, 'We've family we need to ring too. How many people are you ringing?'

I almost shouted, 'I've finished. You can use the fucking phone!' I was so mad. The woman just stared at me. She slowly started to pick up the receiver. I carried on staring at her, then, for one moment, snapped back to reality. *What if she hit me?* I hoped to God she wouldn't put the phone down and come towards me. I thought it best if I walked away. *What am I doing? Jake's not worth getting into a fight over.*

My heart started to race and I looked round for Mia. I spotted her on a phone further down the corridor. I headed over to her and leant against the wall while she finished. *Where was Jake? More to the point, where was Elliot?* Jake should have been at home. On Sunday nights we had tea and watched telly before school and work the next day. I realised it was a bank holiday, which meant no school for Elliot until the following week; still, I expected they'd be at home thinking of me, miserable without me. Not be out enjoying themselves!

Mia came towards me with a big smile on her face. 'Gary's coming to see me soon. He's missing me. He's really upset I'm in here. He's going to bring me some stuff I need, and said he'd help me in any way.' We walked side by side. 'He's stepping up for me, Tilly! I know we've been apart a few months, but he says he really misses me. Hopefully, we'll be back together soon.'

I smiled at her. 'Lovely, I'm pleased for you.' *He could say anything. You're stuck in here, he's out there, doing exactly what he wants.* I thought it best to keep my opinions to myself and not shatter her dreams.

'How's your family?' she asked.

My cheeks flushed. 'There was no answer. I'll ring them tomorrow.' I tried to change the subject. 'I'm going for my meds, you coming?' She chattered on about 'her Gary' all the way there. I just listened.

We turned a corner and came across two officers with a springer spaniel on a lead. It was a beautiful dog, not unlike the one that outed me at Dover customs. It, too, had a white coat with brown liver spots. The two officers - one male, one female - were dressed differently to the other prison officers. Their uniforms were black and red, and very distinctive. The dog just lolloped alongside the officers.

I stared after them as they walked down the corridor. 'Who are they?'

'I think they're the 'black and reds'. Some sort of security,' said Mia. 'They can stop you at any time and search you. Must be looking for drugs.'

I looked at her, amazed. *How can prisoners access drugs in here?*

We passed a room I'd not noticed before; from it came the familiar fragrance of soaps and shampoo. It was full of women in every state of undress. Some had towels wrapped round them while others were clearly comfortable naked. I walked in for a better look and saw bath tubs all lined up against the wall. Finding the bathroom lifted my spirits, and I vowed that I'd have a bath the following day, rather than strip wash from the sink in my cell.

We carried on to the medical hatch, got in line and were handed our meds, after they'd checked our numbers and prescriptions. I was told to collect my next meds after breakfast the next morning. I said goodnight to Mia and went back to my cell.

I was so tired. Though I had little energy, I washed my face and teeth and got my cup ready for the guard on hot water duty. With a little time to sit and think I obsessed over Jake and Elliot, and where they might have been. I felt a sudden rage; they were out and about while I was locked up like some dangerous animal. I thought of all my family and could feel my cheeks burning. *My poor mother and father - I have to speak to them. And what must my grandmother think?* I would miss taking her shopping. Not knowing how long I was going to be in prison was killing me. Added to how ashamed, guilty and lonely I felt, I had trouble even breathing.

I tried to calm myself down. In a way, I was thankful to be on my own in the cell - at least it allowed me to work through my feelings in private. I heard the guard open the hatch; I collected the water and made a coffee. Slowly, I undressed and climbed into bed.

I wanted to sleep but was aware of the loud noises and the constant banging. I tried to be positive.

Perhaps Jake and Elliot had just taken Ellie for her last walk? It was a summer's night, and it was better to take the dog out when it started to cool. I remembered that, although it was only eight o'clock and early evening to them, it was bedtime for me.

Laid on my back on the hard bed, I felt every one of my muscles. I was like a plank of wood, stiff and tense. I tried my best to relax and think of something nice. *Okay...I'm on a white sandy beach. The palm trees are swaying in the warm breeze...I'm laying on a beach towel. Relax...breathe...pray.*

The tablets must have knocked me out, because when I woke, I felt like I'd slept for a week. Mia joined me at breakfast and I felt calmer, like I could get through the day. I collected my meds after breakfast and continued to feel in control. Mia said she felt calmer, too.

We headed to the relevant area to start our first day of work. The room was laid out like a classroom and was full of desks and chairs. It bore a small window at the end of the room, and down one wall sat loads of boxes, piled high. The walls were painted a dull grey, and on one was a large clock; it was dismal, and not helped by the fluorescent strip-lights hanging from the ceiling. A guard sat at a desk under the window. We gave our numbers and names to her and she handed us some sheets that contained numerous address labels.

The guard told us to collect two boxes each and to sit at a desk. Luckily, there were two empty desks side by side - all the others were occupied by women who'd already started working.

The first box contained leaflets from car manufacturers: Jaguar, Mercedes, BMW, Ford, and a few others, advertising their new car launches. The leaflets had to be folded then placed into envelopes from the second box. We were told to stick a label on each envelope. 'I expect you to complete 100 leaflets,' said the guard. *Sounds easy enough.* I started to stuff the envelopes.

It seemed like hours had passed, but, looking at the clock on the wall, it had only been thirty minutes and I was already pissed off. *To think I'm reduced to this... and for £2.50 a day!* It was humiliating.

We worked until 11am, then it was time for outside exercise. We went out to the yard. I needed reviving, stooped over the desk, stuffing those awful envelopes; my neck ached, and it had only been two hours. The dingy room was depressing enough.

I breathed in the fresh air then Mia offered me a cigarette. I'd not had one for days after running out. 'Are you sure?'

'Yeah, it's fine. I'll be getting some more soon. I've been trading.' I just looked at her, confused. 'You have to trade for everything in here.'

'What do you trade with?' She just winked. I savoured the nicotine hit before we headed off for lunch.

After lunch, we were incarcerated until 2pm, then more envelope stuffing. We were locked up again at 4pm. I felt tired and frustrated...the constant locking up every few hours was unbearable. *Who sleeps that much? But what else is there to do? If this goes on for years, I'll go mad!* I didn't usually allow my brain, even for a minute, to explore my fate long-term, as I wasn't sure I could handle the outcome. It felt safer just getting through one day at a time.

I wanted to sleep, but it felt unnatural in the daytime. And I knew if I slept through the day, I wouldn't sleep come night-time. I'd experienced this already; the noise kept me awake the first few nights. The lack of sleep was bad enough, but laid awake, hour after hour, my mind went into overdrive, which was much,

much worse.

I tried to have a nap – I didn't want my brain questioning everything. I wanted to be at home, which made me cry. Then I started to worry. *Is Jake managing? Did Elliot go to work with him? Who's looking after Elliot if he's at home? Is he cooking for them both…? Will he do the washing? Will he get any shopping in?* I remembered that Elliot had a dentist appointment before school started. *What about his school uniform? Will Jake wash it? Does it still fit?*

When teatime eventually came, I was shattered. I needed to be positive, and I needed to talk. I wanted to see Mia and be round a friendly face. And I'd made my mind up: after tea, I was going to have a bath, then try and ring home again.

As we ate, Mia said she hated being in her cell with two other prisoners. 'They're friendly enough…they're just not my type. How did you manage to get a cell to yourself?'

'I'd nothing to do with it. They just put me in there. In fact, I'm surprised no one else has been put in with me. I only recently found out the medical wing contains the detox wing…that's why there's so much screaming and shouting – everyone's coming off the drugs.

'It's not much quieter where I am. There are still those that carry on through the night. Thank God we're now on some meds – hopefully, we'll sleep better.' She looked round to check no one was listening to our conversation. 'Do you think we could ask about sharing a cell?'

I smiled. 'That's a good idea! We could have a word with the doctor, or ask Miss Woods.'

With that thought in mind, I felt a lot better. I took my plate and cutlery to my cell, and grabbed the last remnants of the soap tablet I'd been given on the first day, together with the small towel. I locked my other things away. Mia had gone to get her things; we arranged to meet at the bathroom. I stuffed my key in my pocket, along with the phone card.

When I got to the bathroom, Mia was already stood outside. 'It looks pretty full...I don't know how long we'll have to wait to get a bath.' We wandered inside. Women of all shapes and sizes were either in a bath, washing, or stood around, drying themselves and chatting whilst getting dressed.

A guard appeared from a doorway at the bottom of the room. She waved us over. 'Are you wanting a bath?' she shouted.

There was a lot of noise: water was either streaming into the tubs, or making gurgling noises as the baths emptied. We walked towards her, careful not to slip on the wet floor. 'We both need a bath,' said Mia. 'It's our first since we got here.'

The guard nodded, went into the back room, and came out with two large towels and some tablets of soap. She handed one of each to us. 'Used towels go into that big bag near the entrance. The soap, you keep. If you need razors, I can give you one, but you have to return it to me once used.' I declined, but Mia said her legs could do with a shave. 'There are two prisoners in front of you, then just take a tub when one comes free,' said the guard.

We moved nearer the door where there looked to be some sort of queue; we were also out of the way of people washing, drying and dressing. The place reminded me of our old swimming baths back home. Steam hung in clouds throughout the room; the floor was damp and wet, and water was everywhere. I wondered aloud where we should put our things when we were in the bath; Mia pointed to some lockers at the far end of the room where people were dressing.

It seemed to take forever until a tub was free and we were next in line. Slowly, we undressed, putting our things into a locker, before walking, naked, to a tub. The locker key hung from my left wrist by a ragged strip of plastic.

I took a closer look at the now-available bath tub and it made me feel sick. It had hair stuck in the plug-hole and a tide-mark ring around the edges. I almost changed my mind. I pulled the hair out of the plug, ran a little water and rubbed the sides of the tub to get some of the grime off. I rinsed what I could, replaced the plug and started running my first bath in prison.

Despite the thought that the bath was dirtier than I was, the water was quite refreshing. I bathed quickly and wet my hair, but as I didn't have any shampoo, I couldn't wash it. Getting out, I wrapped the big towel around me and pulled the plug. The dirty water gushed down the plughole. I dried off as quickly as I could and got dressed.

It didn't bother Mia to walk around naked; she'd washed her hair and wrapped the towel around her head in a makeshift turban. I got the impression that she was well aware some of the women were giving her approving looks. Mia was quite tall, about 5ft 8"; she was slim yet curvy...a very striking woman who oozed sexuality. Her skin tone was olive, which complemented her dark eyes and long, straight, black hair. She sashayed, as if she was a top model on a red carpet at some black-tie event. I was in awe that she had so much confidence. She dressed and returned the razor to the guard then we headed for the telephones.

By this time, it was half an hour before lock-up. The queues at the phones were not too long, thankfully, and we both lined up. I got out the phone card and started dialling. I prayed for Jake to answer. After a few rings, the phone was picked up by Elliot. 'Hi, love, how are you?' I said, as if I was just on holiday somewhere.

'Hi, Mum, I'm fine. I've been playing with Jimmy at his house. His mum got the paddling pool out.' I could tell he'd had a good time in his voice. 'He also had some water guns. We had a right laugh with those, but Jimmy got into trouble because he squirted next door's cat. Dad picked me up after work and he got us fish and chips for tea. When you coming home, Mum?'

I gave a hollow laugh, in a bid to stop myself from tearing up. 'Glad you had a fun day. Is your dad there? I need to speak to him.' As Elliot shouted his dad, I heard an automated message that said I only had a few pence left on the card.

'Tilly...how are you doing? I thought you'd have rung last night.' Jake sounded happy to hear from me.

'I did ring last night, Jake. You were out, there was no answer. Don't forget, I'm locked in my cell at 8pm, so I have to ring before then.' There was no answer. 'Jake?' I shouted. 'Hello? Are you there?' The dial tone was dead.

I replaced the receiver. I was so angry and frustrated that the tears started to flow. Mia saw me and came over to give me a hug. 'It'll be okay,' she reassured me. I wanted to scream 'It's not okay!', but I just sobbed into her shoulder.

Eventually, people started to head back to their cells. 'Come on, let's get our meds,' said Mia. 'You'll sleep better and cope with tomorrow if you get a good night's sleep.' Still crying, I collected my meds and said goodnight. I really didn't want to be alone but I had no choice. When I got to my cell I collapsed on the bed. I stayed there even when the guard opened the hatch with some hot water.

I woke up after a few hours, initially unsure of why I was still dressed and on top of the sheets. I had no idea what time it was; drowsily, I staggered to the small window. I opened it and took in the breeze, which soothed my swollen face, after the hours I'd spent crying. I put my puffy face to the breeze and just enjoyed the sensation of the outside world on my skin. I could just see a few stars twinkling in the night sky if I pressed my head against the tiny opening.

I felt exhausted and drained. *I thought those tablets were supposed to stop my anxiety?* At that moment, I truly doubted whether I could carry on. The guilt and shame. Missing my little boy and watching him growing up...missing all my family. It tore me apart how normal Jake sounded – as if nothing was wrong. I wanted to scream, and nearly did. I bit my lip in an attempt to contain it, and splashed my face with cold water. Eventually, I fell back on the bed, hoping I'd be able to sleep.

I woke again when I heard the routine banging of doors. *Back to the nightmare. Will I ever get used to hearing that noise first thing every morning?*

I took note of my smelly, creased outfit; I'd worn it every day since arriving at that hellhole, yet I couldn't have cared less. My mood worsened as the day went on. Mia attempted conversation, and when I didn't answer, she still wittered on – all through breakfast, at work and during lunch. I had no desire to make small talk; I was struggling to complete even the most mundane tasks.

At the end of the working day, just before 4pm lock-up, Mia took me aside. 'I'm sorry you're upset. Is it me? Have I done something to offend you?'

Her expression showed concern. 'No, Mia, it's nothing to do with you. In fact, you've been great. I just want to go home.'

'Don't you go nuts on me, girl! You're the only one from Yorkshire, and the only person I feel I can trust in here. Well, that's assuming you're not already a nut case...'

I laughed. 'Sorry, I bet I've been a right misery today. I'm just at a loss over what to do. Thanks for cheering me up.'

Mia smiled and linked her arm through mine. 'Come on, lass, let's stick together and take this place on, head first. We can beat it.'

If only I could feel as strong as she does...

Chapter Seven

The next couple of days passed in a haze. I was able to tolerate the daily routine without panicking, which made me wonder if the tablets had at last kicked in. I stopped feeling utter despair, but it wasn't as if I was singing from the rooftops instead. If truth be told, I didn't really feel anything. *Perhaps, if I'm numb, like a zombie, I can get through this.*

As the weekend drew near, all I could think about was my family coming to visit. I felt more positive as a result and made the effort to talk to Mia, and anyone else who wanted to chat.

On Thursday I spotted an extra table in the canteen. It was full of supplies that prisoners could purchase. We got our wages the same day; whatever was in our accounts we could spend. I'd earned £7.50 from stuffing envelopes, and the money that had been in my purse at the time of my arrest was also in my account. I think I'd had around £100 on me when I was stopped at customs, but I was aware that the money had to last. I decided to buy a £10 phone card; some tobacco, roll-up papers and a lighter; and a bar of chocolate. I couldn't afford branded cigarettes. *I've plenty of time to learn how to roll up. At least I can still have a smoke.* I felt a surge of relief. Smoking, although a dirty habit to most, always mellowed me.

I decided not to ring Jake that night. I knew I'd get upset talking to him and I wanted to stay positive. Before lock-up Mia and I went to the guards' station and made an appointment to see Miss Woods. We planned to ask if we could share a cell.

We spent Friday morning stuffing envelopes as usual. After lunch, we headed to our meeting with Miss Woods. She asked us a few questions, then said, 'You do know that lesbian relationships are not tolerated in prison, don't you? There are fines and penalties if you're caught.' That made me laugh, and Mia seemed amused, too.

'I assure you, Miss Woods,' I said, 'I'm completely heterosexual, and in a committed relationship with my partner. We just want to share a cell because we're from the same area, and we're both new to the prison system.'

She seemed to accept this, and said, 'I'll see what I can do.'

'Can you tell me what other jobs are available?' I asked.

'Working in the kitchen is always an option. But it's long hours and you have to wear a uniform...a t-shirt and white trousers. You'd start at 6am and work until noon, then again from 2pm to 7pm.'

If we work longer hours, we'll not be locked in our cells all the time...

Immediately, we both said we wanted to apply. 'I'll put your applications forward, but it may take a couple of weeks,' she said. 'Now, is there anything else I can help with?'

'Are there any clothes I can borrow?' I looked down at my grubby outfit. 'I've been wearing these for days and I won't get a change of clothes until my family visits on Saturday.' She showed me to the laundry. In the doorway was a box that contained various tops, trousers, skirts, nighties and underwear that former prisoners had left behind.

I rifled through the clothes and fished out a pair of jeans, a t-shirt, a bra and two pairs of knickers. Though I wasn't thrilled at the idea of wearing other prisoners' clothes, I knew that beggars couldn't be choosers. *I can always bring them back when I get my own clothes.*

On Saturday morning I could barely eat breakfast,

I was so jittery with excitement. I'd taken a bath the previous night, and asked Mia to trade some shampoo for a couple of roll-ups. Maybe it was futile, but I'd wanted to clean off what I felt was the smell of prison before my family arrived. I'd also spent a long time drying my hair; I wanted to look as presentable and like my old self as I could.

After breakfast, we were allowed to watch Diana's funeral on the telly. The room was jam-packed. It was a sobering time - the whole prison seemed to be mourning, but I couldn't take it in. I was sad, just like the rest of the country - especially seeing the two princes walking behind Diana's coffin – but the intensity of the situation only increased my urge to see my family.

When it came time to go to the visiting area, I started to shake uncontrollably; my legs turned to jelly, my palms were sweaty, and my mouth felt like a desert. I was excited but also extremely nervous. *Will they treat me the same? How can we ever be normal with each other, when I've let them down so badly?*

The visiting room was airy and spacious; it housed around twenty circular tables, which had four chairs around each one. Though the tables were spaced out, there certainly wasn't much privacy. I reasoned to myself that, even though other prisoners would be relatively close, at least I'd be able to sit alone with my children.

Down one side of the room was a row of vending machines showing off their wares: chocolate bars, sweets, cold drinks and crisps. There was also a serving hatch, from which visitors could buy tea and coffee for themselves and the prisoners they were visiting.

I sat at a table and waited. I could barely breathe, and I felt as if I was wound tighter than a watch's spring. When Kate and Elliot walked in I started to cry - something I'd promised myself I wouldn't do. Elliot clutched Kate's hand and looked a little frightened until he saw me; he ran into my open arms. I hugged him tightly and kissed his head, overcome with love for this little person. Kate was smiling as she approached but I could see tears in her eyes when she got closer.

'Mum, you're squeezing me too hard. It hurts,' squeaked Elliot.

I laughed. 'I'm sorry, but I've missed you both so much.' I pulled Kate close and hugged her, probably too hard, too. I drank in her smell, and made a mental note to recall how I felt at that exact moment when I was back in my cell.

I eventually let her go and she saw me glance towards the entrance. 'Jake's not coming,' she said. 'This visit is just for me and Elliot. Jake said he can't face coming here to see you...yet. He's just upset - he thinks he's better talking to you on the phone at the moment.' She paused. 'He promised to write soon. And he sends all his love.'

I just nodded, not daring to speak. I felt utterly let down, and anger began to grow inside me. I knew I had to keep my feelings hidden for the time being, to enjoy precious time with my beloved children. Jake wasn't going to spoil it.

We eventually sat down, all wiping away tears. None of us quite knew what to say. Kate looked around at the other prisoners greeting their families then back at me. I noted how sad she looked. 'It was a bit unnerving when Elliot and I were searched coming in here,' she said. 'I had to put my handbag and our coats into a locker, and the bags of things I've brought you. They searched the bags. They said they'd pass on the clothes and toiletries I brought you, but not the magazines and chocolate. Apparently, they're not allowed; I have to take them home with me. They said, if you want magazines, they must be sent to the prison from a designated newsagent. How strange is that?'

Elliot piped up. 'Can I have a drink of pop and some crisps?'

I looked at Kate who already had her purse in her hand - the only thing she was allowed to bring in. She got out some change. 'Do you want anything?' she asked me.

'I'd love a coffee...a bar of chocolate - anything will do.' Elliot grabbed the change and went to the vending machines while Kate bought some coffees.

I watched Elliot as he punched the numbers into the machine. *He's got taller...and his hair's longer.* His dark, shaggy mass of curls shimmered with the light. The back of his hair touched his shirt collar, and I could tell his fringe needed cutting, as he kept brushing it out of his lovely green eyes. I felt a pang of sadness – I always cut his hair. *Now I can't even do that simple thing for my son.* I swallowed as the anger rose up again.

He resembled Jake so much. The thought made my stomach flip, as it always did when I thought of Jake. I smiled as Elliot stared at the vending machine, his face screwed up in concentration as he pondered what to buy. The machine's lights made his freckles sparkle on his tanned face. My heart was heavy. *He shouldn't be in here.* I felt as if someone had just punched me in the chest.

I looked across to Kate. She wore a pretty summer dress that showed off her lightly-tanned arms and legs. Her blonde hair shone, like a halo around her slim face, but she looked drawn. *She shouldn't be in here either.* Another punch to the chest.

'How are you, Mum?' said Kate.

I didn't answer her question; instead, I had to get my apologies off my chest. 'Kate, I'm so very, very sorry. I'm sorry to have involved all of you in this horrible mess. I don't know why I did it. I never thought for a moment I'd get caught...I don't really know what I thought. I was an idiot. I thought it would solve all our problems. It was the money...I thought it was the easy option. I can't believe I've been so stupid.'

She looked straight at me.

I continued, 'It's not just that I've got caught, I know I've to suffer the consequences for breaking the law. The punishment isn't what they do to me in here. It's not being with you all...not having my family around me. It's breaking my heart.' I fought back tears, and quickly took a sip of coffee.

Kate let out a long sigh. 'I'm sorry this has happened. But know that the whole family is behind you. We'll do anything to help you get through this.' She took my hand then got out of her seat and wrapped her arms around me. I nestled my head against her shoulder and silently sobbed. *She smells safe. She smells of home.*

Elliot came back to the table with his booty: a can of pop, a bag of crisps and three chocolate bars. 'I'm so hungry,' he said. 'We set off early to get the train at Wakefield. I had to have a really early breakfast.' He opened the can of pop and took a few large gulps. As he lowered the can, he burped loudly. He looked at me, then at Kate. We all started laughing.

'Elliot, what do you say?' I prompted.

'Excuse me.' Still smiling, he said, 'It was great on the train. We came to Kings Cross then had to take a few other trains. We went on the underground... that was the best! All those tunnels, it was amazing.' I looked into his green eyes - the only thing he'd inherited from me - and had to bite down on my lip so I wouldn't start crying again.

'Well, it's your first trip down to London. It's quicker on the train, and you get to do it all again on your way home,' I said.

He started munching one of the chocolate bars. 'I'll buy some sandwiches on the way home, don't worry about him,' said Kate. She turned to Elliot. 'Don't be eating that too fast, and save one bar for Mum.'

For the next couple of hours Kate and I chatted while Elliot played with some Lego he found in a toy box. Kate took him to the toilet once, then he sat on my knee for a little while. I held him close, even when my legs started to go numb. He told me he was looking forward to going back to school and seeing his friends.

'You'll be good, won't you?' I made him promise.

'Will you be back home soon, Mum? It's not the same at home without you. Ellie's missing you too.'

Kate interjected, 'I think the dog keeps looking for you. When I go round she looks past me, as if she expects you to be there. She's getting lots of love off Elliot, though. He walks her, and she sleeps on his bed now.' I smiled, but the sick feeling in my stomach returned. At that moment, I'd have done anything to go back home.

When it was time for them to go, I tried to be strong - more for Elliot than anything. As they left the room, I waved pathetically and tried to smile until they were out of sight. I sank into a chair, utterly exhausted. I even held onto the table, in case I collapsed and slid to the floor.

A guard came over. 'Are you alright?'

'I feel a bit faint.'

'Lock-up's before tea. I suggest you have a lie down.' I knew she wasn't really concerned about me, she just wanted me out of the room. As I left, I saw Mia with her arms around a man, hugging him close. For the third time, anger flared. Yet, at the same time, I missed Jake. It pained me to think of him.

Back in my cell, I mulled over the things Kate had told me. My mother had teamed up with one of my neighbours, Fanny, and Penny, a good friend; they'd shared all the chores to help Elliot. Mum had checked his uniform and, with my father, had taken him shopping to get him a new blazer, trousers, shirts, and a pair of shoes. Fanny and Penny pledged to cook meals on a daily basis for Elliot after he got home from school, as Jake would be at work. My mother had insisted she did all the washing, and Penny offered to get all the necessary grocery shopping. Kate had got several keys cut, as well as cleaned my house.

I was overwhelmed with gratitude that these wonderful people were helping me. *What would I do if they weren't around?*

Extremely proud of the women in my life, I felt particularly lucky to have such a young, strong and organised daughter. She promised to take Elliot to his dentist appointment and for a haircut. Despite this appreciation for my loved ones, a part of me was seething. I hadn't heard how Jake was going to step up for his only child. Okay, so he'd drop Elliot at school in the mornings, which was always my job, but big deal. He only went to work and back - surely he was capable of more?

Kate had said my parents were going to write. I'd not managed to work up enough courage to ring them. I could imagine my mother saying, 'You made your bed, you have to lie on it,' - one of her favourite sayings. I curled up, sobbing yet again, and prayed. I was full of shame, guilt, and loneliness. The distress washed over me. It almost felt like there'd been a death in the family, with all the grieving. *But I was the ghost, I'd caused this misery.*

My mind was full of different emotions and I found it hard to focus on one thing. *Jake, where are you? Why are you being so useless? Why haven't you been to visit me? Why can't you do more for your son? Why did I ever fall in love with you? What are you going to do to help me, my family, YOUR SON?* I wanted to go to sleep and never wake up. *Please, God, let me feel peace...*

Eventually, the tears stopped. I uncurled and stretched out then went to splash some water over my face. I looked in the mirror above the sink; the distorted version of me stared back. *You have to get a grip. Don't rely on Jake, you can only rely on yourself. Then maybe you can make it.* I'd only been in prison a week; there was a possibility I'd have to endure it for years.

Depressed and sluggish, I went to the canteen. Mia was at the entrance, waiting for me. She took note of the expression on my face. 'I know how you feel, Tilly. It's been amazing to have visitors, but it's a right kick in the head when they leave.'

I just nodded. We linked arms and joined the throng of prisoners. 'I'm not hungry, but I know I've to eat or I'll get ill. I'm going to ring Jake after tea, then get my meds early and hopefully go straight to sleep.' We got our food and ate in silence. As we walked to the telephones, I asked, 'Was that Gary visiting you?'

'Yes,' she said. 'He's going to bring up my two eldest boys next week.' I felt a little jealous – at least Mia's partner had taken the time to visit her.

By the time Jake answered the phone, I was already wound up. 'Hi, how are you?' I said. My tone was sarcastic and cold.

'Tilly! I've missed you so much. I love you. Are you

alright?' His words were slurred. *Oh my God, he's drunk. Or high.*

My voice got louder. 'You bastard...what are you playing at? Why didn't you come and visit me? Are you high or drunk because Elliot's with Kate? You enjoy yourself while everyone else is suffering, why don't you?'

'Look, I'm dealing with this the best I can. I can't come and see you locked up yet. Christ...' He started to cry. 'I really do miss you. I'm a mess...I think I'm having some sort of breakdown.'

'Get a bloody grip,' I screamed. 'It's me in prison, you selfish pig.' I was crying now, too. There was silence. Eventually, I said, 'I'll ring you tomorrow night. Make sure you're home and sober. Goodbye.'

Before I rang off, he said, 'I do love you. Goodnight.'

As I replaced the receiver, I was shaking with anger. Tears fell from my eyes, but they were tears of frustration. I wiped them from my face and looked across at Mia. She was also crying. We didn't speak a word to each other about our phone calls as we went to collect our meds before returning to our cells.

The next morning was Sunday. I woke after a fitful night's sleep. I'd doze off then lie awake, tossing and turning. I had some horrific nightmares.

I looked through the bag of clothing Kate had brought. It was somewhat liberating to put on my own clothes. After a few days with no appetite, I realised how hungry I was. I ate everything before me at breakfast.

My mood lifted slightly as I looked forward to service. I'd not been to church for years, other than christenings, weddings and funerals. I'd been brought up as Catholic, but the religion meant less and less to me as I'd got older. Yet, in prison, I felt that singing hymns and praying could bring me some solace.

The room in which the prison held services looked a bit grim. Naively, I'd expected an altar, pews, and a pulpit – or at least something that represented a church. But it was just a room, like the workrooms and classrooms; the only difference being that all the chairs were lined up to face the front, and there was a cloth-covered table bearing goblets. The priest looked genuine enough in his robes, though.

I took a seat. After a few minutes, I became horrified at what I witnessed. The other women were not there for a church service - they were all busy trading. I saw drugs passed round, money exchange hands; cigarettes, roll-ups, lighters, stamps and chocolate bars moved round the room. Another thing I noticed was how many women were in lesbian relationships – they'd come to service for the opportunity to hold hands and be together. I was stunned. *I can't, even for an hour, get away from prison life and its depravity.* I shut my eyes tightly, bowed my head, and tried to concentrate on the priest's voice.

I rang Jake again that night. There was a strange distance between us. We found it hard to communicate without becoming annoyed with each other, or apportioning blame for how our lives had turned out. I felt I was interrogating him, but I needed to know he was there for me. I needed him to be strong for the three of us.

I had a chat with Elliot, and he sounded as if he couldn't be bothered. He was having an early night as he was back at school the following morning. I came off the phone feeling alone and dejected.

The start of a new week, and I was on automatic pilot. The day seemed to pass in a haze until teatime. Mia seemed as morose as me. During tea, Miss Woods approached us. She was smiling. 'I've managed to get you moved so you can share a cell together.' I felt her news couldn't have come at a better time. I quickly jumped up.

'Can we move our stuff now, before lock-up?'

'Yes, I'll wait here. You collect your things and I'll show you to the cell.'

I could have hugged her, but instead, I said, 'Thank you so much. This means such a lot...thank you for being so understanding.' She smiled as we practically ran to get our belongings.

The new cell held four beds and was therefore larger than the one I'd had, though the layout was the same. It felt spacious and airy. 'Are we in here with other prisoners?' asked Mia.

'Not tonight,' said Miss Woods, 'but that could change at any time. This will probably be your cell now until your court dates.'

We thanked her again and started putting our things in the lockers, leaving out our cups for the last coffee of the day. I felt quite content; it was comforting to have someone else in the room. That night, we were like two kids on a camping trip. We talked all night, and felt that if we were together we could help each other get through this purgatory.

The week progressed, and I seemed to cope better as the routine became more familiar. I tried not to dwell on Jake. I needed to keep a positive attitude to get through each day. I noticed Mia became quieter as the week unfolded.

By Thursday I'd earned enough to buy another phone card. I could contact more of my family, not just Jake. Mia was still vacant.

'Do you want to talk?' I said.

'I feel as if I'm sinking, Tilly. I'm probably coming down with a bug or something. I don't think I'm going to ring home tonight – I'm going to get a bath instead, I think it'll make me feel better.'

'Okay...but you know you can talk to me, right? Anytime...I'm here for you.'

'I know,' she said. 'Thanks.'

That night, when Mia went to have her bath, I rang Kate. I also caught James at home. He surprised me by saying he was coming to visit on Saturday. An avid Leeds United fan, he followed all their away matches, and on Saturday they were playing in London. He planned to visit me before the match. It gave me a boost knowing I'd see him soon.

When I got back to the cell, Mia was sat on her bed, looking miserable. I decided not to tell her about James's visit. As I stepped further into the cell I saw a woman by the bed that was furthest away from the door.

She stared at me, which was quite intimidating. 'Hi, I'm Tilly. Have you just arrived?'

'It's my first night, I'm on remand. I'm Sally.'

Her accent sounded Welsh. She looked to be in her mid-forties; she had cropped blonde hair, and was quite thin with a round face. She continued to stare. Her expression seemed aggressive, even threatening.

I looked away. 'Well, I hope you sleep well tonight. If you have a cup, they'll be round soon with hot water, so you can have a hot drink before bed.' I turned to Mia. 'Do you feel better after your bath?' She nodded and got out her cup.

We made our drinks then Sally started talking. In fact, she wouldn't shut up - we got her life story. She'd been living with her boyfriend at his house, and according to her, everything had been fine until his elderly, sick mother had to move in with them. Sally had tried to persuade her boyfriend to put his mother in an old folk's home, but he was having none of it.

Sally said she'd helped out with his mother at first: dressing her, washing, and cooking for the old girl.

But after a few months, she'd become fed up with it. She gave her boyfriend an ultimatum: either she left, or his mother did.

He chose his mother, and as you can imagine, Sally was upset about that. She set fire to the house, which burnt down quickly. Her boyfriend and mother had been in the house as it perished. She tried to convince us that she'd not done it, that she'd not set fire to the house. I felt the hairs on the back of my neck stand up. *My God, I'm sharing a cell with an arsonist. What if she thinks we're not treating her well enough – will she burn us, too?*

'Accidents happen,' I said nervously. 'I'm sure everything will turn out okay.'

Mia said nothing. I decided to get into bed. I got my nightie out of the locker, went into the toilet and got changed. I climbed into bed and heard movement, which I assumed was the other women following suit. I opened my eyes to see Mia settling under her sheets. I couldn't see Sally, and assumed she was undressing in the loo.

I couldn't sleep. *I'm sharing a cell with someone who's killed two people!* I felt like I had to keep one eye open, just in case.

Chapter Eight

I tossed and turned for a while then had the urge to go to the toilet. I peeled back my sheets and opened the toilet door. The light was on, and to my horror, there was blood everywhere. It was on the walls next to the toilet, all over the floor, and against the door. Lying on the floor was a razor blade. I picked it up; it looked tiny and blunt. It dawned on me what had happened. *Mia's stripped it from a safety razor and slit her wrists.*

I ran from the toilet and pushed the alarm button on the wall. I shouted to Sally, 'Look under Mia's sheets! I think she's slit her wrists.' I banged again and again on the cell door, shouting for the guards.

Sally slowly sat up in bed. Again, I shouted, 'Look under Mia's sheets!'

'Why should I?' she snarled.

Still banging on the door, I screamed, 'I can't do it, I need to get the guards' attention.'

After what seemed like hours, the hatch slid open. 'What's all the noise?' said the guard.

'Mia's slit her wrists! There's blood everywhere. Open up the cell!'

'Calm down. I can't open cell doors after lock-up...I need a master key. Are you sure about Mia?'

I turned round to see Sally lifting Mia's sheets. 'Yeah, she's slit her wrists,' she said. 'I don't think she's conscious.'

'Oh my God!' I screamed at the guard. 'Please open this door and get her some help!'

Another guard came; once she learned what was happening she went for the master key. I knew, at that moment, that if anything was to happen to me, I'd die in there. They were in no hurry to help.

I didn't know what to do. 'Please can you hold my

hand?' I pleaded. 'I'm really scared.'

The guard took in my distress. 'Put your hand through,' he said, and I tightly held onto him. I knew it was odd, but it made me feel as if I was on the outside, like I had a connection to the outside world. It helped me feel safe.

It must have been at least twenty minutes before two guards opened the cell door. They pulled a stretcher on wheels into the cell. Pushing past me, they went to Mia's bed and looked under the sheets. One stood at the top of the bed, and one at the bottom. They counted to three and pulled Mia onto the stretcher, wrapped up in the bloodied sheets, then wheeled it out.

I pleaded again with the guard holding my hand, 'Can I just stand for a few minutes outside the cell?'

He looked up and down the corridor. 'Okay, I'll stand with you.'

I struggled to control my breathing. 'Mia will be looked after,' the guard reassured me. 'She'll be fine.' After five minutes, he said,' You have to go back in your cell now. I'll bring you some hot water for a cuppa. You look like you need one.'

'What about the blood in the toilet?'

I saw him cringe. 'I'll bring some cleaning equipment. You'll have to do it, I'm afraid.'

When I went back into the cell I saw Sally in bed, asleep. *How the hell can she sleep after that?* The guard brought the cleaning things and I approached the toilet, armed with a mop, a bucket of hot water, a cleaning rag, and a tablet of bleach.

The guard followed me in. He shook his head when I handed him the razor blade Mia had used. 'Empty the water down the toilet when you've finished with it,' he instructed, 'and leave the mop and bucket by the cell door.'

As soon as the cell door was locked, the tears started again. It seemed so inhumane. *Why do I have to wash all this away? What if Mia has AIDS? How desperate must she have been, to attempt suicide?* I filled the sink with water and dissolved a bit of the bleach tablet onto the rag. Carefully, I wiped the door, the wall tiles, and the loo, which were all covered in Mia's blood. I then mopped the floor until it was all gone.

I sat on my bed, Sally's breathing the only sound I could hear. I was angry that she was able to sleep.

I drank my tea. For some reason, my mind kept playing the Eagles' song, Hotel California, over and over. *You can check out any time you like, but you can never leave...* I knew there was no way I'd get any sleep. *Please, God, please make sure Mia's alright... don't let her check out.*

Eventually, I got into bed. I laid flat on my back, unable to relax. Even though I could hear Sally's snoring, it just made it more apparent how lonely I was. I tuned into the usual nightly noises in the background and felt drained. I'd assumed Mia was a strong, confident woman. *How wrong was I?* I was surprised at how worried I was about her. After all, I didn't really know her that well, yet we had a connection, strengthened due to the dire circumstances we were in. Was I really that bad a judge of people and their characters?

I started thinking about the first time I met Jake, and my eyes pricked with tears yet again. I could even remember what he'd worn, and the dress I'd had on. I'd felt confident in it, and all my friends said it suited me. It was a soft mint-green colour, which brought out the colour of my eyes. It was figure-hugging, but not low cut. It had lovely flowing sleeves that formed a bell shape at the bottom.

I'd been on a night out in town with my friend, Jenny. At the third pub we visited we met a group of people, some of which Jenny knew. They were going on to a house party and they invited us to join them.

At the party, Jenny started talking to a guy. I watched the others dance and chat, but after a while, I got bored with being ignored, so I went into the kitchen for another drink.

On the table were various bottles of alcohol. Humming to the music blaring out from the next room, I started to pour a gin. I looked in the fridge for some tonic water, holding onto my dress at the back as I bent down - I knew my knickers would be on view otherwise.

Behind me, I heard a whistle. 'Wow, that's a sight for sore eyes.' I straightened up to look at who'd made such a chauvinistic comment, and I admit, I almost swooned.

Stood before me was the most handsome man I'd ever seen. He had dark hair and a cheeky smile, and he wore a blue fitted shirt with the sleeves rolled up, tucked into his tight-fitting jeans. I felt my cheeks flush. He looked about the same age as me. His deep blue eyes twinkled and he smiled approvingly as he looked me up and down.

I shyly smiled back, and took a large gulp of my drink for courage. The gorgeous man walked towards me. 'I'm Jake. What are you drinking?'

He must have thought I was dumb or stupid, because all I could manage was a smile. Eventually, I managed to say, 'Erm...gin and tonic. Do you want one?' Glad of something to do, I started pouring. 'I'm Tilly.'

We chatted for some time, laughing and flirting...I'd not felt that good in years. He said he had to leave and my face fell, but he asked for my number, saying he'd like to keep in touch. I gave him the salon's phone number. He bent to kiss my cheek, then left. I watched him walk away…maybe it was the drink, but I felt breathless at the sight of his pert bum in those tight jeans.

I found Jenny, who was still talking to her guy. I said I wanted to leave, as I had work in the morning. She agreed; she said her goodbyes whilst I phoned for a taxi. On the way home we were both in high spirits – she'd arranged to see her guy again and was excited. *That's fine – she's single. But I'm married… what was I thinking?*

At least I'd not arranged to see Jake again, but nevertheless, I felt like I was floating, just because a handsome man had made me feel alive. I felt like a teenager, and couldn't stop giggling.

I tried to put it out of my mind; I didn't expect Jake to call, but I did enjoy reliving our meeting – it brought a modicum of excitement into my predictable life.

A couple of days later, Jake called the salon. 'When can we meet up?' he asked. Before I knew what I was saying, we'd arranged a time and a place. *There's nothing in it…we're just meeting up for a drink. It's okay.*

I played with fire when I should have put it out. After our date, that was it…I was in love - hook, line and sinker. I couldn't get enough of Jake, I thought of nothing but him - I couldn't stop myself. I'd been well and truly swept off my feet.

That's not to say I didn't feel guilty about sneaking around with Jake, because I did. But I justified what I was doing. James and Kate were teenagers living their own lives; they no longer needed me. My husband also did his own thing; we rarely did anything together. We virtually lived separate lives. We'd slipped into a boring routine and our only connection was living under the same roof.

Things soon became very real, however, and quite ugly. After a few months, my husband, John, found out. I'd told everyone I was going out with friends when I was really with Jake. I came home at 1am in the morning; I quietly undressed then got into bed, assuming John was asleep.

He switched on the light. 'Where have you been?'

'Where do you think I've been?' He just looked at me. In that instant, I had to make a decision: continue to lie to everyone, including myself, or have the courage to come clean. 'I've been out with another man and he's the love of my life. I want a divorce.'

John ran into the bathroom and threw up. I felt so bad and ashamed. I followed him into the bathroom. 'Look, I'm sorry...can we talk about this?'

Before I knew what was happening, he'd grabbed hold of my hair and started dragging me round. 'You fucking whore!' That woke up the kids.

There was even more hell to pay. 'Why are you doing this to Dad?' screamed Kate. I didn't dare say anything else. John rang my parents, who arrived an hour later. I got dressed, made some coffee, and sat in the kitchen to have a cigarette. I saw the dog cowering under the table with all the commotion. John was shouting and pacing up and down. The kids had gone back to their rooms, both crying their eyes out.

'How long have you been carrying on?' my mum asked. My father said nothing. She carried on, 'You, lady, have got a family. You're going to work this out – you're not going anywhere.'

Still I didn't say anything.

John grabbed my arm and swung me off the chair. 'Get your bag and coat, I'm taking you to your boyfriend's,' he spat. Mum tried to calm him down, but he pushed her out of the way. 'I don't want her here. She can go to that bastard.'

He dragged me out of the house; as soon as I got in the car he roared away and drove like a lunatic. I was so scared and just hung on to my bag and coat. By now, it was about five in the morning.

John only spoke to ask the address. As he pulled up outside, he sneered, 'It looks like a doss house. Now, get out.' I climbed out, hoping against hope that Jake wasn't in.

John banged on the door, shouting, 'Come out, you bastard, and get your whore.' In all the time I'd been married to him, I'd never heard him use such language, nor seen him so angry. I just stood, shaking. *What have I done?*

Jake opened the door. He looked worried, but ready for a fight. I really hoped it wouldn't end in violence.

'Here she is, she's all yours,' shouted John, thrusting me towards Jake. Then he got in the car, revved the engine a few times and screeched off.

I was frozen to the spot. Jake put his arm round my shoulder. 'Come on, lass, let's get you inside.'

I let him guide me into the house. I was numb, I couldn't think. Jake made a cup of tea and we sat in the kitchen in silence, which I appreciated after all the drama. He pointed upwards, indicating that he was going to bed. I followed him; we got into bed and cuddled. I clung to him tightly until I finally dropped off to sleep.

The next few months were emotional, and passed in a blur. I moved into Jake's rented house and the divorce was partitioned. The kids decided to stay with their dad. Mum and Dad didn't speak to me.

I'd been enthralled with Jake, and truly thought he was my soulmate, that he was worth it. That didn't stop me feeling bereft at the upset I put my family through.

After a few weeks, relative normality ensued, and

I began to feel that everyone had come out the other side intact.

As life settled down, the kids came to visit, along with my father. As part of the divorce settlement, John kept the marital home. He paid me my share, and after I sold my hairdressing business, Jake and I bought a house together.

A few years went by. I was very happy with Jake, and he was over the moon when Elliot was born. Mum came back into my life, and I honestly believed I had my 'happily ever after'.

Our perfect life was shattered by Jake's gambling. It wasn't just the financial mess we'd been in. Life changed, fast. I'd tried to sort things out in the conventional way: I worked extra hours, cut back, and restricted what we spent money on. But we were still sinking.

One car was about to be repossessed, and the mortgage was in arrears. I'd been at my wits' end. If I thought that was hardship, I'd had no idea. Due to one disastrous decision, I was now in a living hell, away from all my loved ones. If only I'd thought it through... *What was the worst that would have happened if we'd lost it all? At least we'd have been together.*

***

I hadn't known Tony that well. The first time had been on Jake's birthday, and we only went out with him and his crowd a couple more times. Tony never mentioned again that he could help me out, and I didn't bring it up when we were in company.

I still had his card, but couldn't summon up the courage to ring him. I wondered if he even remembered giving me it.

Looking back, I agonised over why I didn't listen to my instincts. I knew I didn't trust Tony, from the first time I'd met him.

Jake had been seduced into a life he wasn't accustomed to, or could well afford. He'd got out of his depth, mixing with those people. He'd never taken cocaine before, or gambled to that extent. Jake wanted the life Tony had, but there was no way he could ever emulate it. I suppose everyone, at some point, thinks the grass is greener elsewhere.

I considered asking Mum and Dad for financial help, just to get us out of our fix, then repay them one day. I decided against it; my mum would never have let me forget how I'd let such a situation occur.

With no other options, I wondered what Tony would say. What solution he had. *Would it hurt to just ring and find out?*

After a week of dithering, I rang Tony and asked if the two of us could meet. He sounded pleased to hear from me, if not a little hesitant; he never asked why I called, though, and we arranged to meet at a restaurant for lunch the following week.

I dressed conservatively: black trousers, a white blouse and black jacket. I didn't want to give Tony the wrong impression. Even though it was a hot, sunny day, and I felt a bit drab in black, I chose the outfit to send the message: *this is strictly business.* I got to the restaurant on time; it was the new 'in' place, and quite swanky. A young waitress showed me to the table where Tony was already sat with a glass of red wine in front of him. He smoked a large cigar.

The table was in a partially-covered patio area not far from the entrance. It had a brightly-coloured parasol and a good view of the whole place. It was easy to see who was coming in or leaving the premises. I think Tony picked it for that reason.

He stood up on seeing me, and leaned over to kiss my cheek.

'What would you like to drink?' asked the waitress.
'A glass of wine, please.'

I sat next to Tony, so I had the same view of the
place as he did. 'It's a lovely place,' I commented.

'Yeah. I've been here a few times. Great food and
service, and it's not as expensive as people make out.'
He was dressed casually: khaki jeans, a beige short-
sleeved shirt, and beige open-toed sandals. He looked
very tanned.

He wasn't traditionally handsome, yet he had a
presence - a confidence, and a very charming smile.
He had closely-cropped blonde hair and his eyes were
dark brown. I imagined he could be quite menacing at
times.

The waitress came over with my glass of wine and
asked to take our food order. 'Can you give us a few
minutes, sweetheart?' said Tony. We engaged in a
little small talk; we asked about each other's partners,
and chatted about the times we'd all been out.

I started to relax a little. We looked over the menu
and made our choices. The smells wafting from the
kitchen were intoxicating, and made me feel quite
hungry.

The sky was a lovely deep blue; white fluffy clouds,
resembling cotton wool, passed by on the gentle
breeze. I could feel the heat of the sun - it was pleas-
antly warm, not too hot or sticky. One of those rare
summer days that made you feel glad to be alive.

I ordered a salmon and prawn salad whilst Tony
went for a medium steak. The waitress left, and immediately, Tony got down to the business. 'So, Tilly, why
did you want to meet me on your own?'

I took a moment to find the right words. 'I'm just
curious...you said, when it was Jake's birthday, that
you could help me. I don't know if you remember. I
said we were in a bit of a mess, financially, and you

gave me your card as we left your house.'

He smiled, nodding. 'Yes, I remember. You were a bit on edge, if my memory serves me correctly.' I shuffled uncomfortably in my chair. 'Jake had a good time that night,' he continued. 'He was either drunk or high. That was when you met us for the first time -I suppose it was a bit awkward. You were the only one sober, for a start.' He started laughing. Despite myself, I laughed along with him.

Our food arrived then and we began to eat. After a minute or so, Tony looked round the whole restaurant before leaning in and speaking in a whisper. 'I know I'm blowing my own trumpet, but I'm a damn good businessman. I own one of the biggest scaffolding companies in this area. But, erm, let's just say some of the things I do...and some of the contacts I have... They're not entirely...legit.'

I must have looked confused, because he sighed and continued to explain. 'I'm not a drug dealer, and I don't distribute drugs across the community. I just arrange shipment...from the supplier to the dealers.' He chewed on a large chunk of steak. 'I'm a middle man. It's just business.'

What the...? I found myself nodding as he talked, but inside I was wrestling to not look shocked at his candidness.

'I only use people I can rely on - not young, inexperienced kids. My success rate speaks for itself.' He looked smug. 'No one I've used has been caught. No one has been stopped, or even suspected.' He wiped his mouth with his napkin.

'Mistakes,' he continued, 'are only what other people in the business make – but not me. They use the same people over and over again to collect...send them to the same destinations. Now, that's wrong. If someone travels to the same place more than, say, four times a year, it looks suspicious. Your average worker only gets one or two weeks' holiday a year.'

I was becoming hot, and I knew it wasn't just down to the weather. I scanned the restaurant myself, to make sure no one was listening in. *Had I heard him correctly? Was this what he was talking about when he said he could help me?*

'If someone travels regularly, they can usually prove they're on legitimate business and need to visit the same place for one or two nights at a time. Because, otherwise, it gets noticed.' He paused. 'Look, this doesn't even have to be an issue. I change my couriers frequently - you can do one job for me and leave it at that. Or, you could go to different areas, if and when I need you to. It's completely your choice.'

So, that was what he was offering. Tony clicked into salesperson mode. 'You're the ideal person, Tilly. You are Mrs. Average...someone who's never been in trouble with the law. You're well presented, you have life experience – especially as a mother. I'm sure you'd be able to deal with any situation. No disrespect, but no one would look at you twice. You're perfect for the job.'

His voice was calm, steady, cajoling and reassuring. He made it seem like we were discussing an office away day for a company who always topped the sales charts. He was getting into his stride now, and leaned even further forward. 'I can arrange for you to do a short trip...like a trial run. You'd collect half a kilo of Class A from my contact in Belgium. I'll pay all your expenses, like your hire car, ferry fares, your petrol, food, and so on. And, when you get back, and I'm in receipt of the goods, I'll give you a thousand pounds. Not bad for a couple of days' work.

Tony had a voice like velvet. He complimented me, and made me feel invincible. I'd been nervous about meeting him alone, yet as I sat there, I couldn't think why. In such beautiful surroundings, eating delicious food, and with such an attentive companion...I began to feel heady. *From the wine?* Tony made everything sound so easy. And there was no denying the thousand pounds would go a long way to getting us back on track.

I didn't know what to say next. Thankfully, Tony said, 'Take a day or so to think it over. If you do want to go ahead, I'll give you all the details.'

'Thanks, Tony,' I said. Then I had a thought. 'If I do...you know, go ahead, I don't want Jake to know about any of this.'

He just nodded. 'Of course, I understand. That goes both ways.'

By now, we'd both finished our meals. The waitress came over and reeled off the desserts on the specials board. 'Or would you like to see the menu?'

I looked at Tony, then at the waitress. 'Just coffee for me, please,' said Tony.

'Make that two,' I added. As she scuttled off to get them, I wasn't sure what to say next. 'Have you any holidays booked?' I asked.

'Jackie and I are going to the south of France for a week. We'd stay longer, but we've a wedding to attend back here.'

I started scrambling in my handbag for my cigs and lighter. Tony must have thought I was looking for my purse. 'Don't worry about lunch. It's on me. I'll ring you in a couple of days...I'm sure we can work something out.'

Chapter Nine

The dull-grey prison walls crowded my brain. I wondered how long it would be before I'd get to taste food as good as that meal had been. I salivated at the memory of the succulent prawns and creamy salmon. *That's why you're in here, you idiot. You thought you could just smuggle drugs into the country and carry on as normal.* It still bewildered me that I'd been so naive, so misguided. *So arrogant to think I'd get away with it, because I looked so...so... How did Tony put it? So 'average'.*

Sally was snoring like a pig. I got up and walked over to the window. It was just beginning to get light, and I reckoned it was about six in the morning. I lit a cigarette and blew the smoke into the fresh air. I felt tired, and extremely fed up. Most of all, I was angry with myself. I'd had a good life, and now I'd ruined it. It was my fault I was in prison, I got that. *But if it hadn't been for Jake's antics, we wouldn't have been in a mess to start with...* I took a long drag of the cigarette.

Sally followed me as I went down to breakfast. She asked loads of questions about Mia. I tried to remain polite, but I didn't want to talk about it. Sally spooked me; I didn't like the woman at all. Thankfully, she had to go for her induction whilst I was at work. I tried to avoid her at lunch.

As soon as I'd eaten, I sped to the medical wing to find out how Mia was. 'We can't give out medical information unless you're a family member,' the guard told me.

How ridiculous! I pleaded with them to pass Mia a message. 'Just tell her I hope she recovers quickly.'

I missed talking to her. I didn't trust Sally, and I kept my lighter with me at all times when we were alone in the cell.

Saturday came. After breakfast, I had a quick strip wash in the cell, then changed into some jeans and a bright green t-shirt I'd not yet worn whilst inside. It was oddly important to me to wear something 'untarnished' before seeing my boy. My excitement built.

The moment I saw James turn the corner towards the visiting room, my breath caught in my throat and my chest tightened. I smiled as he approached and fought back tears. He spotted me and waved, before jogging over to the table. I stood up and he flung his arms around me, then lifted me up and swung me round. It felt like we were celebrating something.

He let me down gently and kissed me on the cheek. 'Mum, we miss you so much.' I saw that his cheeks were flushed as we sat opposite each other. I wiped away tears of happiness, but I couldn't speak as my throat was so dry.

James placed my hands in his. 'I'll get a drink. Do you want a coffee?' I could only nod. He went to the counter to get our drinks; however much I felt sorry for myself, I was full of pride for my firstborn.

He set the coffees down and took my hands again. Looking straight into my eyes, he said, 'How are you coping?'

I mustered all the conviction I could. 'I'm struggling. But I promise you this, I will get through this. I'm so utterly ashamed. I'm so sorry for bringing this mess to all of you. Please forgive me.'

James squeezed my hands. 'Do you know what the number one single is at the moment?' Without waiting for an answer, he said, 'The drugs don't work, by The Verve.' I wasn't sure what he meant by that. *Was he angry with me? Would he ever forgive me?*

'If you were going to commit a crime, why could it not have been a white collar one? Why drugs, Mum?'

I stared blankly at our hands and shook my head. He withdrew one hand and started to drink his coffee. I followed suit. 'James... I didn't know what to do. The person I turned to for help convinced me it was easy. He said there'd be no risk or ramifications. I just had to collect a parcel from one place and deliver it to another. I thought it was that simple. I didn't think of the drugs. I didn't think of the consequences, come to that. And I certainly didn't think I'd get stopped at customs.'

I took a deep breath. 'Never in a million years did I think I'd end up here. But, what's done is done - I've got my comeuppance. I'm sorry for being so stupid... all I can say is, I've got my punishment. Believe me when I say I regret how it's hurt you and all the family. I am deeply, deeply sorry.'

James didn't address what I'd said; instead, he excused himself to go to the toilet. My heart was in my mouth...I thought he'd walk out and not come back.

I anxiously waited for him to return, sipping at my coffee in a bid to calm down. Within a few minutes he sauntered towards the table. He sat down and held my hands again. 'I know you're going through a horrible time. I forgive you. We just want you home...we all love you.'

I kissed him on his cheek and he wiped away my tears. I looked in awe at the young, big-hearted giant of a man in-front of me. Though he resembled my ex-husband, I also saw my father in him.

We chatted about the football match he was heading to, how his work was going, what his friends were up to, and their antics when they were all out together. He made me laugh, something I hadn't done for a good while.

Saying goodbye, not knowing when I'd see James again, was heart-breaking. I held back the tears until he'd left the visiting room. I glanced round - others were suffering too now their families had left. It was a very different atmosphere to when we'd arrived, excited at the thought of seeing our relatives. Now, we were all in tears. At that moment, I hated that room.

Sally wasn't in our cell when I got back, to my relief. I changed into different clothes; I wanted to keep those I'd taken off for visits only. I was happy that I'd seen James, but now felt extremely alone. Gut-wrenching sadness swept through me. *I need to keep busy.* I put the clothes in my locker and spent a few minutes sorting its contents, when in walked a guard with Mia. It didn't look like she was really with us; she was like a zombie.

The guard led her to her bed and sat her down. Mia was the same colour as her stark-white sheets. I was shocked at how ill she looked.

I sprang up and wrapped my arms around her, hugging her tightly. 'How are you?' The guard smiled smugly. I'd already been warned about that warden; apparently, she was bad tempered and cruel. Some even called her perverted.

I immediately withdrew my arms. 'Shouldn't Mia be in the medical wing? She doesn't look at all well.' I tried not to sound as angry as I felt.

The guard smiled again. 'What, you don't want your girlfriend back? Got a new one, have you?'

I ignored the taunt. 'Look how sedated she is! Can she even eat or drink? And her bed isn't made...how's she supposed to do that?' I could hear my voice getting louder but I couldn't stop it.

The guard took a few paces forward, until her face was inches from mine. She pushed me against the wall and prodded me in the chest. 'Don't you raise your voice at me! I'm the boss in here. You're just scum, you dumb bitch.'

Her huge belly pressed into me and I struggled to breathe. Her lips puckered, and for a brief moment, I thought she was going to kiss me. Instead, she raised her hand. I shut my eyes, expecting a slap across my face.

She grabbed my hair at the base of my neck and yanked my head back. My head banged against the wall. I wanted to scream. She must have sensed what I was about to do. She pushed harder against me. 'Go on...scream. No one's going to come and save you.'

She pulled at my hair again. 'This prisoner has been discharged from the medical wing. She will have to make her own bed, as always - unless you want to be a sweetie and make it for her.' I could feel her spittle on my face, as her sweaty body crushed me against the wall.

I stared at the guard then at Mia, who'd not moved. I started to sob. *This is hell.* The guard let me go then ambled out of the cell, with that smug smile still plastered on her face. *Could she have been more heartless?*

It was nearly teatime. I talked quietly to Mia, who stared right through me. I linked my arm through hers, gently raised her from the bed, and guided her to the canteen. It took ages, as she was only able to shuffle. She leant on me heavily.

I sat her down at a table then realised I'd not brought any implements to eat with. I left Mia at the table, ran back to the cell and collected what we needed. I queued for our food, balancing both plates, and decided to fetch our drinks after we'd eaten.

Mia was motionless. I put food onto a fork; she opened her mouth and chewed slowly. I tried to snatch a mouthful of my own food, before it went cold, as I fed Mia. It took a long while - by the time

Mia had stopped eating, it was nearly time for lock-up.

'Mia, would you like a drink?' She slowly shook her head and tried to mumble something. She was either too upset to speak, or so drugged up she was unable to. We slowly made our way back to the cell.

Sally was already in bed and snoring for England. I was thankful – I didn't have the energy for her questions. I made Mia's bed, got her into her nightie, and helped her into bed. By this time, I was worn out. My arms and back ached; I thought I'd fall asleep as soon as I hit the pillow. Instead, I tossed and turned, upset and appalled at the way Mia had been treated. The doctor had discharged her, and now I had the responsibility of looking after her.

The following week was tiring, as I continued to help Mia. Sally never offered to help, not that I wanted her to; I was glad she kept a low profile. I really didn't like her. Thankfully, by the end of the week, Mia had improved enough to eat, wash, dress and walk unaided. She was certainly nowhere near her normal self, and I began to wonder if she ever would be.

The following week, she resumed work, and even joined in the odd conversation. By now, I felt worn out. I wasn't sleeping properly, I still worried about Mia, and it took all my effort to survive. It was like my spirit was slowly being dragged out of me.

Weeks passed in a fog then Mia and I received some good news for a change - news that I hoped would help Mia return to normal. Our application to work in the kitchens was accepted; we'd start the following Monday. It meant that we'd be out of our cells for longer, and we'd get a uniform of white t-shirts and trousers. It sounded better than hours of stuffing envelopes.

The next Monday, we were let out of our cell at

05.55am; we usually had to wait until much later. We walked into the large kitchen where we were met by a huge man, who turned out to be Gerry, the chef. He was welcoming and friendly, thankfully. He showed us around, introduced us to the other workers, and explained our duties.

At our stations were racks of produce that we had to prepare and put into a large container, which resembled a plastic skip. It appeared an easy job. How wrong that assumption was! On that first day, we had to chop salad. We rinsed loads of cucumbers, tomatoes and lettuce then chopped them all up, mixing in the lettuce we'd shredded. It was hard work that strained our necks, arms, legs, and backs.

That said, the good points outweighed the bad. We had our breakfast in the kitchen, which meant larger portions. We could have plenty of cigarette breaks, and Gerry left the code for the phone on his desk in plain sight. After a few days, the other kitchen workers told us that, when Gerry was on his break, there was the opportunity to sneak into his office, crawl under the desk, and use the phone for free. You just had to make sure he didn't catch you in his office.

Another perk, we learned as the weeks went by, was the opportunity to grab a couple of sandwiches as they were made; these, you slipped into your bra for later. The danger with this was getting past the 'black and reds'; if you weren't stopped or searched by them, you could trade the sandwiches to other prisoners.

I loved being in the kitchen. It was less restrictive; you didn't feel watched all the time – though they were strict on things like giving out knives, which you were made to hand in after use. I certainly ate more, and being out of the cell for longer helped me gain a sense of purpose. It beat promoting car companies. Mia became stronger, too.

The atmosphere in the kitchen was wonderfully informal. Probably, for the first time in my life, I met women from different cultural backgrounds. In most cases, this was interesting, and certainly humbling - but sometimes, it was frightening. A lady called Mona, from Nigeria, who was only in her twenties, told us she was on remand for bringing in drugs from Africa. Her life story was horrifying.

She described her hard life in a small village, which included walking miles to fetch water. She told of the trauma she went through when some men arrived from another village. They ransacked her home, raped the women, and shot some of the men. She was ordered to smuggle drugs, or her family would be killed.

That gave me perspective. She was caught with the drugs at Heathrow Airport, and now awaited trial. She didn't know if she'd be deported, and if so, if she'd return to find her family slaughtered. I had no idea how she found the will to live.

Some of the African women, including Mona, conjured up spells, and put 'hexes' or 'ju-jus' on the prison guards and the customs officers who'd caught them. If any of them had court dates approaching, they'd include the judges in their voodoo. It was scary, but also quite comical.

As we learned more, it transpired that Mona had come into the country with a kilo of drugs, yet her 'charge' was for a half a kilo. This seemed common: many prisoners said the amount they'd brought in had been reduced when they were charged. *Where did the rest of the drugs go?*

It wasn't as if a prisoner would correct the authorities, as their sentences would be harsher as a result. It seemed the perfect crime. *How are customs officers any different to us? So, they wear a badge...they still profit from imported drugs.* The injustice stung.

A few weeks drudged by. I received a letter from my solicitor. He would visit the following week for a meeting about my court date. This brought my anxiety to the surface again; I was terrified of going to court. I dreaded hearing what sentence would be given for the crime I committed. Using inmates' tales as a measure, I faced being in prison for ten years. That thought made me shake and, on one occasion, throw up.

The morning of Mr. Hewitt's visit came round. I couldn't face breakfast, I had an excruciating headache, and I visited the toilet countless times, due to my nerves.

I was escorted to a room and found the solicitor already seated, drinking coffee. 'Hello, Tilly, take a seat.'

He gave his friendly smile, which put me at ease. 'How are you?' I asked politely.

'Very well, thank you. Busy as usual. I hear you now work in the kitchens...do you like it?'

I tried to sound positive. 'Yes. It's better than I thought it would be, thanks.'

We went through some formalities. Mr. Hewitt told me that a court date had been set; it was three weeks away. 'Because it's your first offence, bail might be an option.' I stared at him, wide eyed. *I might be out of here soon!* That shifted my universe. I think he regretted telling me that, as I stopped listening to him.

I snapped back to reality when he brought out a file that contained my court papers, my statement and the charge I faced. '...smuggling one-quarter kilo of Class A drugs,' he said.

'One-quarter kilo? Not a half-kilo?'

He paused and reread the charge. 'Apparently, the drugs were of poor quality. They weren't pure enough, so the quantity was reduced to one-quarter kilo.'

'So, where do all these drugs go, from the police or customs, if the amounts are constantly changed?

Who monitors that? Do the authorities use the excess drugs themselves?'

He ignored me and pressed on. 'Let's not bother with that question - just be thankful the amount has changed in your favour. I'm going to set up a meeting with your barrister before the court date, so we can see how he's going to present your case.' Before he left, he added, 'Ask for some more medication, if you're anxious, Tilly. I'm on your side.'

Ten days later, Mr. Hewitt came again, with the barrister, Mr. Strictly. The latter was a giant of a man, with a posh, booming voice. He stood as straight as a ramrod, his large chest and belly waddling before him. He looked a cross between a large toad and a wise owl.

His tweed suit was obviously tailor-made; from the pocket of his paisley waistcoat hung a large, gold, antique fob watch. He wore a red dicky-bow, and a red handkerchief poked out of his breast pocket. He had a full head of silvery hair, which was cut short at the back and sides, and a face I'd call 'lived in'.

Perfectly enunciating the queen's English, his voice was deep and booming. He was someone my mother would refer to as a 'proper gentleman'. I'd never met anyone like him.

Introductions were made, then to my surprise, Mia walked in. Apparently, her solicitor was from Mr. Hewitt's company, and it had been decided that Mr. Hewitt dealt with both of us - because we'd both been arrested on the same day, and for the same crime. Our trial dates also coincided. Mia had come straight from the kitchen; she didn't know anything about the meeting until Mr. Hewitt gave her a letter from her original solicitor.

Mia and I had already worked out that we'd most likely carried drugs for the same people. We'd never met on the outside, though we lived just ten miles apart. We knew the same people, either through work or social gatherings. She'd had her trip arranged by someone different, yet we'd been given the same contact in Belgium from whom we'd been told to collect the drugs.

Mr. Strictly sifted through our files until he found my statement and the charges I faced. The two lawyers went through my statement; hearing them discuss it brought the same pang of pain into my heart, at how recklessly I'd forfeited my liberty from that fateful trip. As they talked, my mind wandered to my follow-up meeting with Tony, after our initial get-together at the bistro – the point where my journey to utter misery began.

I'd left it a few days before contacting Tony. 'I want to go on a trip,' I'd said.

'Someone will ring you tomorrow with details,' he'd replied brusquely. By the time the phone rang the next day I was a nervous wreck.

The voice on the other end of the line made my stomach churn. 'Er, hello, Macca,' I said, as politely as I could.

'How you doing, Tilly?' his whiny voice had a lewd tone. 'I hear you're doing a favour for Tony. I'll have to give you the details in person. When's best for us to meet up?'

I cringed. The man was a grade one slimeball, and well-known in our area. I was disappointed that Tony dealt with Macca, but even more disgusted that I had to deal with him, too.

'Tomorrow, after 10am, is best for me,' I stuttered. 'Where?'

'Meet me at the market hall, next to the betting shop. See you at ten...I'm really looking forward to seeing you.' I heard him chuckle as he finished the call. I just shuddered. *What an unpleasant man!*

I'd met Macca a couple of times before. He popped up sometimes when Jake and I had an evening out. On reflection, they were the nights out that Tony arranged. I didn't think he was a particularly close friend of Tony's, as he seemed to pay him little attention and always left before everyone else. And it was Jake who'd introduced me to Macca. Regardless, I'd instantly disliked him. He'd looked me up and down, as if he was undressing me with his beady eyes.

His name was Douglas Macdonald, but everyone knew him as 'Macca'. There was just something about him that made me feel dirty. He thought he was God's gift...forever putting his arms around women's waists, trying to touch them up. He was short and wiry, with dirty, greasy long hair; he always smelled of sweat and booze. He was usually dressed in the same t-shirt, jeans and leather jacket. Unfortunately, whenever our paths crossed, he'd make a beeline for me - it made my skin crawl, and it was enough to keep his hands off me and remain polite. I wasn't looking forward to meeting him, especially as I'd be on my own.

It was raining by the time I got to the market hall. I spotted Macca and walked towards him. I dodged quickly into the coffee shop, to avoid Macca's out-stretched arms.

I sat at a table and asked if he'd like a coffee. He shook his head. 'Let's get down to business, I don't have much time.' I nodded but still went to the counter and ordered one for myself. I needed the caffeine. I returned and sat opposite him, so he didn't have the opportunity to get too close. To my relief, he was all business.

He looked round the coffee shop, then stared outside for a few moments before passing a carrier bag over the table. 'Everything's in there, Tilly. Don't open it until you're at home and alone. There's travel money, ferry times, the contact number you need, and some hotel addresses in there. If you need anything else before you set off, you phone me. Okay?'

I grabbed the carrier bag and quickly peered inside. I saw an A4 envelope and two road maps then became aware that I was holding my breath. I placed the bag by my feet. 'I'm sure you've thought of everything, thank you.'

He just chuckled. 'I'll see you soon. Welcome aboard! Good luck, though you won't need it...a smart lady like you will be fine.'

He got up from the table and leaned over swiftly, kissing me on the lips before I had chance to back away. I just stared at him as he swaggered out the door. Then I rooted for a tissue in my handbag and frantically wiped the man's kiss from my lips.

***

I tuned into Mr. Hewitt as he read the statement I'd made at Dover. Because I'd said I was guilty, I didn't have to name the person who'd given me the details of the contact in Belgium.

I'd made an instant decision to not involve Tony; I was scared of him and I worried what he could do to Jake and my family. I'd not known the full name of the person in Belgium; he was referred to as 'John', if that even was his first name. The contact gave me a phone number to ring when I got back to the UK, only things didn't go to plan.

The customs report, from when I was stopped and arrested at Dover, stated that an informant had told officials I was on my way to the ferry. No wonder they searched my car. I didn't ask who the informant was, but according to the file, 'John' was being watched by the European department of Interpol; after I'd left his address they followed my car through France and

and alerted the customs at Dover. For weeks afterwards, I'd wondered if my arrest was down to good police work or if I'd been used as a decoy, so Tony and Macca could commit a bigger crime elsewhere.

The whole episode at customs was a blur, as I'd been hysterical most of the time. I couldn't remember the finer details of my interrogation, so I'd forgotten what I'd told them. I'd admitted smuggling drugs, but said I'd got half a kilo of cannabis on me – for some stupid reason, I must have thought that better than admitting I'd brought Class A drugs into the country.

Shuffling his papers, Mr. Strictly said, 'How clever are you, Tilly?'

I blushed. 'I'm not sure what you mean.'

He folded his arms across his vast chest, leaned back in his chair, and stared at the ceiling. 'Do you consider yourself quite clever?'

Quietly, I replied, 'I'd like to think I'm not stupid.'

'Let me put it this way. You've admitted to smuggling half a kilo of cannabis - is that the truth? Can you convince the prosecution of that?' I looked at him, unsure whether I should speak. He continued, 'You see, you have to be very, very clever to trick the prosecution barrister. They've seen everything, and they know when they're being lied to.'

He took a sip of water from his glass. 'If you did bring in cannabis - or you genuinely thought it was cannabis - and you go to trial, you might be believed. You'd probably serve, say, two to five years. But, if you brought in Class A knowingly, and you tried to make them believe you thought it was cannabis... if you were found guilty of false testimony, you could end up serving thirteen years.'

The penny finally dropped. I had to come clean, but I wasn't sure how to say it.

Mr. Strictly gave me the answer. 'If I were you,' he

boomed, 'as it's your first offence, and hopefully only offence, I would plead guilty to Class A drug smuggling. Show you're sorry, and that you'll take your punishment, and you should expect a sentence of between two to five years.'

Mr. Hewitt took over. He said I was to present at a 'Newton Trial'. This was one not attended by a jury; it would be a trial of defence against prosecution, with judgement made by the appointed presiding magistrate.

The men then turned to Mia, and proceeded to go through her file. They told me I could leave, and I waited for the escort guard to collect me.

Chapter Ten

Two weeks on, and our day in court arrived. Mia and I were to appear at Canterbury Crown Court. We were allowed to travel by taxi with two guards; they'd deemed us both too anxious for the 'meat wagon'. Thankfully, I'd been given extra medication. Though I felt calmer, I continually felt sick.

Any other time, I'd have revelled in being out of prison and being on the other side of the prison gates. Instead, I was subdued, and absolutely dreaded getting to court.

The two guards accompanying us were swapped to court security on arrival - they probably went off and had a meal somewhere. Initially, we were put into a holding cell underneath the courthouse. As we left Holloway, we'd both been told to collect our personal belongings - the things that were taken from us as we'd arrived there. These bags were put into lockers next to the waiting cells.

I'd put on jeans and a jumper, and all my jewellery, which made me feel more human. I was hopeful that, as we'd been given our belongings back, if I got bail, I could be home that night. The thought swam round my head like a whirlwind.

The hardest part was waiting in the cell for the trial to begin. Mr. Hewitt had seen us when we arrived at court before bustling off, saying he'd be back later. The wait took three hours, though we were given cups of tea and were allowed to go to the toilet. I paced round the cell, then sat and waited. Eventually, Mr. Hewitt arrived, looking quite forlorn. He said the case had been postponed. We were going back to Holloway.

I dropped my head and cried. By the time the guards came to escort us back, I felt numb - like I was just a body...a shell.

Back at Holloway, we were allocated a different cell; thankfully, it was just a two-bed. *No Sally!* I offered a prayer of thanks. Mia hadn't uttered a single word since leaving court and stayed silent. Again, we had to go through the palaver of getting blankets and other provisions, as well as handing over our jewellery and possessions - all of which were put back into large envelopes with our prison numbers on them, ready for when we finally left. *I can't keep going through this.*

By the time December rolled around, I'd got used to drifting through days in a fog; perpetual crying, the norm. I felt lower than I ever thought possible. The only thing that kept me going was my family. Kate wrote to say she would visit, along with Elliot and James. I was also told Jake had put in a visitor request.

On visiting day, I experienced the usual rollercoaster of emotions: love and sadness at seeing my children. They were naturally looking forward to Christmas, but were clearly upset that I'd not be with them. I tried to be strong. Thankfully, my mother, grandmother and father had promised them that they'd enjoy a wonderful family Christmas.

Kate mentioned that my grandfather hadn't been well. A thought jumped into my head. *Had I caused his illness?* It took some time before I realised I wasn't the cause of every bad thing. I promised I'd write to all the family, particularly my grandfather.

A week passed. Though the kids' visit had perked me up, I couldn't wait to see Jake. I'd not set eyes on him since August. We'd only spoken on the phone – and felt a lot of anger, on both sides - but I still needed to see him. At the same time, I didn't want to see him. I was so mixed up.

When he arrived he looked as handsome as ever. He looked quite tanned, like he'd been on holiday. I shut the thought down sharply. I tried to look calm. I'd washed my hair, worn clothes I'd not worn before whilst inside, and made every effort to feel as normal as possible.

Jake was half-smiling, half frowning, as he walked over. My legs shook so much, I couldn't have got out of the chair if I'd wanted to. He bent down and put his strong arms around me, lifting me against him. I managed to put my arms around his neck and we kissed. It was not a passionate kiss, but a loving one.

He pulled away and gave me a chance to breathe. I clung to him, leaning against his strong body. I could feel him shaking. 'Tilly...' He spoke softly in my ear, and I started to sob.

'Hi,' I whispered.

I clung on to him for a few minutes. Eventually, he said, 'I'm going to sit you down now, my neck's starting to hurt.' I gave a small laugh and let him ease me into the chair. He sat opposite and we held hands over the table. I gazed into his eyes. He seemed shy and awkward.

'You look well, considering,' he said. He shook his head. 'I still can't believe what you did.' I just froze. My mind turned cartwheels; I didn't dare speak but felt my blood begin to boil. *How dare he?! He hasn't even asked how I'm coping. He hasn't been to visit me, even though I've been in this hell-hole for months. How could he say that – in here, of all places?*

I bit my tongue and struggled to steady my voice. 'So, how are you?' I asked.

He looked down at our hands. 'I'm coping with work. Elliot seems okay, but he obviously misses you. Help from the neighbours and your family has made it easier.'

I counted to five. There was no hint that he even missed me. 'Could you get me a coffee, please, Jake?'

He let go of my hands to search his trouser pockets. 'Sure. I think I've got enough. Do you want anything to eat?'

'A chocolate bar would be nice. It doesn't matter which.'

As he walked to the counter I told myself to be nice. *It's his first visit, don't have an argument.* But I couldn't ignore how disappointed and angry I felt. It hit me how lonely I was. Jake may have been there physically, but I didn't feel his support, his love, or even that I mattered to him. *Do I really know him?* I thought I did. I thought he was the love of my life. At that moment, I didn't feel any connection with Jake. *Please, brain, stop muddling things up.*

He returned with coffee and biscuits. I was at a loss as to what to say next, I felt so overwhelmed. I took a sip of my coffee whilst he chewed on a biscuit, then I put my head on the table and started to sob – which was something I did at the drop of a hat most days.

Jake moved his chair closer and took my hands. 'Don't cry, Tilly, it'll be okay.'

I lifted my head and, through gritted teeth, said, 'It's not okay! I'm drowning in here. I just want to come home.' I pulled my hands from his.

He shook his head and sighed heavily. 'Well, it'll be some time before that happens. You're in here because you did a stupid, stupid thing.' It took all my strength not to slap his face. He could see I was angry, and tried to grab my hands. 'Look, we're in this mess now. Let's not fall out. It's taken some organising to get here, I really don't want to fall out.'

I counted to ten before sinking into his chest. 'Why haven't you visited me before now? I needed you.'

He bent his head to whisper in my ear. 'I couldn't come. I couldn't bear the idea of you being in here, I had to get my head around it. Plus, I've had to work extra hours, now we haven't your wage coming in. I've had to look after Elliot and the dog. Look, I'm here now. I'm sorry – okay?' I felt cocooned, with his arms around me. Calm, but numb.

Jake told me about his work, and how Elliot and my family had mucked in and helped. Then conversation dried up. I didn't want to say any more...I was tired, sad and angry. Jake seemed happy to just sit and hold hands. He mentioned that he'd left some postage stamps with the guards, which Kate had given him, so that I could write. When visiting time was up he gave me a kiss, told me he loved me, then walked out quickly. It was like he couldn't wait to get out.

I was hurt. Jake, of all people, should have known how I felt. He had, for a short time, been in prison - years ago, as a young man. He knew what it was like and what it did. Why is he not there for me? The sick feeling in my stomach made me shake. Why is it, when we're happy and life is good, we don't stop and take note of our feelings? Yet, when we're unhappy, we're acutely aware of how utterly miserable we are.

***

Christmas Day arrived. I received some cards, a notebook, and some magazines, from my family and Jake. I locked everything away, including the cards – I didn't feel like displaying them in the cell. I felt like I was in an alternative universe.

No Christmas tree or decorations, no shopping for presents, no menu planning. I desperately missed my family. Without a doubt, spending Christmas in prison was heart-breaking – for everyone.

I spent most of Christmas morning queuing to use the phone. There was a spattering of Christmas spirit: no one tried to push in the queue, and there were no disparaging remarks about those using the phones. The underlying mood was sombre. The women with children on the outside were particularly subdued, morose even – clearly missing their families.

I wished all my family a Merry Christmas. I loved hearing their voices, but the ache to be with them left me feeling alone and empty. I consoled myself with the thought of Christmas dinner in the prison kitchen, presided over by the prison governor. We had the works: succulent turkey with stuffing, roast potatoes and parsnips, loads of veg and lashings of gravy, followed by Christmas pudding and custard. It was easily the best, most nutritious, and by far the largest, meal I'd eaten in Holloway. The governor was pleasant, and he thanked all the kitchen staff for producing the meal.

New Year, and Mia and I were taken to Canterbury again. We arrived at court, waited around, only to learn that the trial was postponed yet again. On that occasion, I found out that my mother and father put £500 forward as bail; because the trial was cancelled, they lost their money. I didn't even get to see them. I was breaking under the burden of what my family was going through.

Corralled in the court cells, I was with another prisoner awaiting trial. She was a sullen figure; for some time she just stared at Mia and me, before asking for a cigarette. As we smoked, I asked her which prison she was in. 'Holloway,' she said.

I prattled on about the food, the guards...anything. I was nervous. Mia just rolled her eyes, as if to say 'shut up'.

The woman said her name was Beth. She was around twenty-five, tall yet stocky, and dressed in a long black skirt, a black shirt, and black studded boots. Her hair was black, and she had a few tattoos. *Some kind of Goth?* She wasn't unfriendly, but neither was she pleasant. We were taken back to Holloway, and Beth arrived in the meat wagon shortly after.

Mia and I deposited our valuables, collected our supplies, and were marched to a cell. This cell had four beds. Beth was put with us. As we started to make up our beds, Beth just sat on hers, watching. I became a bit pissed off at this, but carried on making the bed.

In a quiet voice, she said, 'I shouldn't be in here. I should be in the medical wing.' She got out her own cigarettes and just sat there, smoking. Mia didn't say anything; I decided to keep quiet and went into the toilet.

I returned and started to get changed for bed – it was soon going to be lock-up. Beth started shouting, 'I need to be in the medical wing!'

I snapped, 'Why don't you tell the guard that then?'

She glared at me. 'If I stay in here tonight, I'll kill you both.'

'What?' I gasped. I looked at Mia who'd frozen on the spot. I don't think either of us believed what she'd just said.

Beth calmly repeated herself. 'I'll kill you both.'

I ran to the cell door to call for a guard. I spotted one locking doors further up the corridor and ran towards him. 'That girl, Beth, in our cell, has threatened to kill us.' He just looked at me like I was mad. 'She says she should be in the medical wing.'

He continued to slam cell doors shut. 'She wants to move out of the cell or she'll kill us,' I screamed.

'Calm down,' he said, unconcerned. 'She's probably just messing with you. You'll be fine.'

My breath caught in my throat. 'No, you don't understand. She means it.' He kept walking and we neared our cell. I felt my heart race. 'Please move her,' I pleaded.

He shook his head. 'I can't move anyone now. It's lock-up, there's no time. You have to stay in the cell you've been allocated."

I lost it. I screamed at the top of my voice, 'ANYONE, EVERYONE! If you can hear me, my name's Tilly, and my friend is Mia. If anything happens to us tonight, make sure you tell the News of the World, or The Sun, or the news-people on the telly. We were murdered in our cell because the guard won't move the woman threatening to kill us.'

The guard grabbed my arm. 'Go into your cell.'

I shrugged him off and carried on shouting. 'I'm not going in there! I'm being threatened.'

Two more guards ran up. 'What's going on?' one shouted.

'She said she's going to kill us tonight! She should be in the medical wing.'

The guard walked into the cell and asked Beth and Mia what was happening. I followed and pointed at Beth. 'Tell him what you said to us.'

Slowly, she said, 'I'll kill you two if I'm not moved from this cell.'

The guard grabbed Beth roughly by the arm and led her out of the cell before slamming the door shut. I was on edge and couldn't settle. I lit a cigarette and sat on my bed. Mia had her head in her hands. 'Can I get in your bed tonight? I need to be held; I can't believe how scared I feel. Will you hold me?' I asked.

She slid over to the far side of the bed. I finished my cigarette and climbed in next to her, shuffling up as closely as I could. She wrapped her arms around me. We were both crying.

***

Within three weeks we were back at Canterbury Court. No members of my family or Mia's were present. Finally, it was our day of judgement. During the trial, I kept my answers brief and tried to convey the remorse I felt. I admitted bringing in Class A drugs. I was told the amount had been reduced from half a kilo to a quarter-kilo. I didn't bat an eyelid – it wasn't as if I was going to argue over the quantity.

The judge finally sentenced me to five years of imprisonment. Mia was also given five years. Mr. Hewitt was pleased. He said he'd be in touch.

No bail, so I was shunted back to Holloway. Soon, we'd be transferred to another prison, once arrangements were made. All I could think was: *five whole years! My God!*

I knew it could have been worse. *But five years! How am I going to survive?* We carried out the same scenario back at Holloway: collected supplies, marched along to another allocated cell. Except, this time, the guard told us to report to the medical wing after we'd put our things in the cell.

We did as we were told. After waiting outside the doctor's room I was called in first. 'I need to check you out. How are you feeling? Have you any suicidal thoughts after your sentencing?' I sat on the examining couch as he placed a stethoscope on my chest before checking my blood pressure. I hadn't said a word. 'Are you still taking your medication?'

I looked up at him and started to cry. 'Yes,' I mumbled.

'Your heart rate is a little high, and so's your blood pressure. I'll prescribe more sedatives.'

I just nodded and returned to the corridor. Mia walked past me, into his room. I waited for her. She looked as bad going in as I felt when I came out. *I hope she's okay.* When the doctor had finished with her, we slowly walked back to the cell in silence.

Though I was exhausted, I automatically made the bed. I laid on it; I couldn't be bothered going to the canteen. I didn't think I'd be able to keep any food down anyway; I felt weak and queasy.

Mia slowly climbed onto her bed, fully clothed. 'Goodnight,' she said quietly.

I could tell she was crying. 'Goodnight,' I muttered, not sure if I'd be able to sleep.

The cell door was still open. Despite all the hubbub, I think we'd both zoned out into our own little worlds. Just before lock-up, a guard came to the cell and began messing about with something outside the door. I got up to see the guard putting up a plastic plaque in a metal holder, to the left of the door. It read 'LTI'.

The guard was one of the more friendlier members of staff. 'What's that, Marg?' I asked.

'It means 'long term imprisonment'.'

'Does that have to be there?' I pleaded. 'I don't think I can cope seeing that. Could you remove it? Please.'

She looked at her shoes and sighed. 'Rules state it should be there. You might be moved soon. Forget about it for today.' Despite her words, she took down the plaque and walked away. I went back to bed.

Still awake after a couple of hours, I lit a cigarette and opened the small cell window. I stared at the bright, full moon; it looked to be made from solid silver. It had an even brighter, yellowish-white halo; the wispy grey clouds only enhanced its glow. I was transfixed.

As I smoked my cigarette, the sky changed. Black clouds gathered, blocking out the moon's glare. The blackness appeared to make a shape...a hand, or rather a palm facing down - its fingers, which spookily splayed outwards, made it look like the 'hand' was pushing downwards.

Its five fingers represented the five years I had to serve. It was a message: *you will stay where you are for five years...* The hand seemed to grow into a long-fingered claw with talons. An evil being, delighting in tormenting me. I shuddered and a shiver went down my spine. I shut my eyes, said a quick prayer, and looked back to the night sky. There was the bright moon again, the black clouds dispersing, wafting away slowly with the breeze. Tears ran down my face as I closed the window.

I wearily climbed on the bed. *How can the justice system be right?* I'd learned a lot about my fellow prisoners, their crimes and their sentences, over the last few months. *I've got five years, yet a prisoner in the same court as me, on the same day, who tortured and nearly killed someone, got ten years. How can that be?*

I thought about the times when we'd entered the reception at Holloway. The large television that hung on one wall was usually switched on with the sound blaring out - supposedly, to help calm prisoners down and give them something to watch as they awaited body searches, rationed supplies, and details of their cell allocation. But, when prisoners came back from court, if one of their stories was being reported on the news, the television was turned off - thus protecting the identity of that prisoner. It was futile; everyone knew then that the person on trial was in that prison.

The trial that had caught the media's attention wasn't mine or Mia's. It involved a woman that had discovered her husband was having an affair. The girl entangled with the husband was only sixteen years of age. The wife, aged forty, kidnapped the girl and took her to some woods.

There, she tortured and mutilated the teenager. She beat the girl, stabbed her multiple times, then inserted a broken glass bottle into her genitals. She was reported to have said, '...to make sure the little whore doesn't enjoy sex again.' The wife drove the girl – who was barely alive - back home, dumping her on the doorstep. The girl committed suicide not long afterwards. *How come I got half the sentence of that deranged, dangerous woman? Was I deemed half as dangerous?*

I hardly slept that night. My thoughts swam around, everything jumbled in my mind. I made a decision. My grandmother had sent me a small notebook. It had lined paper and a spiral spine; though it bore no dates, I was going to use it as a diary. It was the only way I could think of to keep my sanity intact. My days would be drawn out...endless...over the next five years.

Monday Jan 19 1998

Sentenced, for five long years. There was nobody in court for me. No 'family'. A lonely start. I felt numb.

Feb 9

I was told I'd be moving to Style Prison, Wilmslow. I was looking forward to the move. It was an open prison; it had to be better than Holloway. Going back north gave me some hope; I would be nearer home territory. It would be easier for the kids to visit.

The journey there was pleasant - it was almost like being on a social trip, though my handcuffs reminded me it was nothing of the kind. In a surreal way, I felt a little excited. The bonus was that I could see the passing countryside from the bus's big windows. Much better than travelling in the meat wagon.

Mia and I were fixated on one prisoner sat near the front. She looked to be about seventy-five years old. On the seat next to her sat a bird cage, which housed a bright blue budgie that happily chattered and squawked throughout the whole journey.

We knew, because of the bird, that the old woman was a 'lifer'. She'd probably served around twenty years in prison, and was now being released to an open facility. I wondered what she'd done, but knew better than to ask. Mia kept imagining her crime, but I just watched the bird. *Why does the system believe it's a help to see a bird in a cage, when you're also incarcerated?*

We arrived at Style. It looked like a stately home, though we knew we were on no tourist trip. The largest of the Victorian buildings had originally been an orphanage. Surrounding the extensive grounds were metres of wire fencing. I consoled myself with the fact that, inside the high wire walls, there were trees, plenty of lush grass, and lovely countryside.

There was a boiler tap in the kitchen, for hot drinks. Just like at Holloway, we were each allocated a pack of coffee, tea-bags, powdered milk, and sugar – that was to last a week. Common practice was to have a hot drink with each meal. The kitchen was locked up from 8pm to 8am, which annoyed me no end. It was something I could never get used to – not being able to have a coffee whenever I wanted one.

At lunchtime, we were typically served a pre-made sandwich or soup; there wasn't an extensive menu. For tea, there'd likely be the thinnest, saddest looking fish fingers, with peas and powdered potatoes, which was laughingly called mash. Or you were sent the cheapest-ever baked beans, with beef-burgers or sausages. It had probably all been frozen for centuries; we never received fresh fish, meat or vegetables. Nutrition for prisoners was obviously not on anyone's agenda. Sometimes, though, we got a treat: Marks and Spencer's biscuits to share. All out of date.

Feb 13

I feel like a wounded animal with nowhere to go. I'm so lonely. I knew I should have felt grateful, being in a semi-open prison. In Holloway, I was constantly alert, watching everyone, always looking over my shoulder. Anxiety 24/7. It was exhausting, always being on your guard. Here, I could relax slightly. But, although the sense of being caged had eased, I felt even more trapped, mentally.

Feb 16

Elliot came to visit. It was lovely to spend all day with my boy, to gaze at his face and drink in his smell. *God help me, I miss being a mum so much.* Elliot was being protected by the rest of my family, but even so, I wondered if I'd damaged my boy by being away from him.

April 1

Kate's twenty-first. I spent the day crying. I felt like my heart would truly break. *God protect me. How will I ever make it up to her? What mother isn't with her daughter on her twenty-first birthday?* I rang to congratulate Kate, and wished her a happy day. I hoped she wouldn't pick up on how distraught I felt. She listed all the wonderful presents she'd received, babbling excitedly, describing how she was going to spend the day: firstly, lunch out with the family at our favourite local restaurant. 'Grandad's treat,' she said. Later, she was going partying with her friends.

May 6

My birthday. I received some lovely cards, but not one from Jake. It was one kick after another with him. Upset, I rang home just before lock-up. When he answered, I could tell he was drunk. 'Hi, Jake, how are you?'

'I'm fine. Happy birthday,' he muttered.

'I've got quite a few cards from the family, but I've not had one from you.'

'Shut up, knobhead,' he said.
I put the phone down, raging with anger.

Chapter Eleven

May 29

Mia's a bit naïve, I can see that now. Like Chinese whispers, the gossip doing the rounds involved Mia. Apparently, after a family visit, she'd let slip to one of her housemates, Shelley, that she'd got some drugs. She told Shelley that she'd swallowed them.

Shelly forced Mia to drink shampoo. Unsurprisingly, Mia had vomited. The women had inspected the contents of Mia's stomach, but found no drug packet. They weren't satisfied and became inventive. A long, hollow handle was removed from its mop-head and rammed up Mia's bottom. Water was flushed through her insides, to make her defecate. Still no drugs were found. I don't know what she got from that experience. *Has she always been that way?*

Rumours about Mia were frequent. I'd dismissed the story I heard of her having sex with the male guards. That is, until I saw her after a shift; she worked in the guard's kitchen.

'Hi Tilly,' she said as she passed. I saw love bites down one side of her neck. We'd been in separate houses a while now, and I was glad we were no longer associated if that was what she was doing.

I'd heard the term 'jail bent', but I hadn't witnessed it in Holloway - the most I'd seen was the secret hand-holding during church services. I could never envisage myself, however desperate I was, having a lesbian relationship. It seemed irrelevant; my libido had upped and left once I entered prison. Later, occasionally, I experienced urges just before my period. During these rare times, and once I'd made sure everyone was asleep, I privately and silently masturbated under the sheets. I yearned for the same ecstasy I enjoyed when making love with Jake. Predictably, the moment of release was inadequate, and left me feeling pathetic and sullied.

The nightly routine meant lock-up was at 8pm. The doors to the kitchen/dining room, and the TV room were locked, as were the outer doors. Time in the evening, therefore, went slowly, and it was usually spent in the dorms. Some women laid on their beds, trying to sleep, some chattered away in groups. Others did God knows what in the bathroom. You were left to amuse yourselves throughout the night; the guards didn't come back until the next morning, unless an incident called for their presence in the night. That usually meant a torch thrust in your face. They'd usually leave again after a head count.

On this particular night there was Lisa, Joan, and two new girls in our room. I didn't know their names – I didn't want to know. They scared me. One of the girls was in a bunk above me. Everyone eventually climbed into their bunks and the lights were turned out. Suddenly, I saw the other new girl cross the room; she headed straight for my bunk. I nearly screamed, and I braced myself to fend her off. To my great relief, she climbed, ungainly, onto the top bunk. The subsequent sex noises were disturbing. They sounded unnatural to me, and left me terrified. I couldn't sleep, and felt sick as the bunks rocked. I cried into my pillow. I was tired, ashamed, and my head was in bits. *This is all because of what I did. I have to live with it.*

June 13

I became closer to my housemates Lisa and Karen. They appeared to be 'normal' ladies, whatever that meant. We helped each other, and I thanked God for them both.

Lisa was a strong woman who'd been at Style for a

year. She'd committed fraud. An educated lady, who could string a sentence together, she was quiet, with no hint of attitude.

She was ten years younger than me; slim and pretty, with big brown eyes and a short, blonde bob. I felt at ease with her. I especially liked her high-pitched laugh - it immediately made you giggle when you heard it. I knew, deep down, that I couldn't trust anyone in there, but all the same, I needed someone to talk to. A bonus: she wasn't a drug user. Like me, she just smoked cigarettes.

Karen was tall - about 5ft 9 inches. She was a stocky lady, not particularly fat, just solid. She had strawberry blonde, naturally wavy, long hair, which she usually wore in pigtails. She had blue eyes, which I thought were too close together – she almost squinted when she looked at you. She was loud, with a quick wit - always ready with a smart remark. And she seemed to smile a lot, which made me suspicious.

June 14

The house is so full of friction. We all have off days, no more so than in a place full of women whose liberty had been taken away. In such close proximity, tension was hard to avoid. Arguments frequently erupted.

Donna and Nicky fell out. Normally, I steered clear of those two - they were the ones who'd had sex in the top bunk. Donna, I guessed, was about twenty-five years old. She was roughly thirteen stone, and five feet tall. She sported a skinhead haircut, swore too much, and she looked and smelt dirty.

Nicky was her total opposite. She was approximately forty, and was just four feet tall; she was ultra slim, with long, shiny, blonde hair. Her perfume was always overpoweringly strong.

I think they'd been together a long time. There was

shouting all through the house. Nobody else got involved, even when Nicky tried to include Pauline in the argument.

As for Pauline, I couldn't tell her age. She was a hardened drug user, and probably younger than she appeared. Her arms were bruised with old injection tracks. She was super skinny, with a heavily-lined face; her hair was long, greasy and lank. Her teeth were rotting, and she had a few missing. She had a thick Liverpudlian accent and kept to herself most of the time, though it was clear she was struggling without drugs.

Joan, originally from Manchester, was twenty-four. Medium build, her long hair always scraped back in a ponytail, she wore thick-rimmed glasses and had prominent buck teeth. I think she'd been bullied at many points in her life. She spent most of her time with young Maz, a goth punk.

July 4

My boy's birthday. *James, I love you. I think of you all day.* As the months passed, I felt left behind by the adults in my life. My children, however, were pillars of support. I owed them everything. *God, keep them safe for me.* Jake only brought me heartache and worries from home. He wasn't there for me. He didn't visit. Things could never be the same between us. *Where is he when I need him?*

July 20

I spent my first day in the sewing room. I'd never had any inclination to sew at home. I think the most I'd ever done was putting a few buttons back on clothes when they'd come off. When I was young, my grandmother taught me how to knit, but I didn't continue with it when I got older.

And yet here I was, sewing uniforms. They were easily recognisable, from a large supermarket. After one particularly hard day, I swore I'd never be a customer in their stores again.

I carefully ran the machine down the seams. After a few errors, I'd got the hang of it. It was mundane work, but it offered better pay. And you could chat with the other women; it wasn't as isolating as being in the kitchen.

July 23

Received my 'wages': £7.50 for a week's work. I'd become quite good at trading in Holloway. I offered my hairdressing skills; everyone in Style knew I didn't want to trade for drugs or sex. I traded postage stamps, tobacco, chocolate, sweets - and most importantly, phone cards. Kate sent me stamps every week. I could sell a book of stamps, worth £2.60, for a £2 phone card.

The most sought-after thing in Style, though: drugs. I saw young and old scrabbling around for foil on which to burn heroin. Wrappers from chocolate bars, foil from aspirin wrappers...they'd do anything for foil as well as the drugs. The house I was in was supposed to be drug-free, but I soon found that not to be the case. But how could I be judgmental, when the reason I was there came down to drugs?

July 25

My grandad died today. I felt tormented and had nightmares. *Please, someone help me.* Lisa and Karen were fantastic, as were the staff, especially Sister Marie. I didn't want to spend a day like this with strangers, but what choice did I have?

I'll never forget today. After being officially informed, I rang my father. He was distraught. Mum wouldn't talk to me, as usual. I don't think I can cope with any more upsets. Sister Marie said prayers with me, and offered to organise a service. After prayers, on returning to the house, I saw Pauline and Donna fighting over cables from someone's radio, to use as tourniquets for their drugs. I wanted to scream, 'My grandad's just died!'

I desperately tried to block out the noise. I laid on my bed and became aware of a tune on someone's radio. It was 'Reflections of my life', by Marmalade. I started to hum along to the lyrics:

The changing of sunlight to moonlight,
Reflections of my life,
Oh, how they fill my eyes,

The greetings of people in trouble,
Reflections of my life,
Oh, how they fill my eyes,

Oh, my sorrows,
Sad tomorrows,
Take me back to my own home,

Oh, my crying,
Feel I'm dying, dying,
Take me back to my own home,

The world is a bad place...

I couldn't listen. I pushed the pillow over my head to shut everything out and sobbed my heart out.

July 30
I found out today that Mia had had a threesome with Kay and Shelley. They were in the bathroom, appar-

ently, having sex. I'd done the right thing, keeping my distance from Mia. I didn't want to be tarred with the same brush.

July 31

It was my grandfather's funeral today. *It's horrible enough to be away from my family, but on a day like today...* The prison staff showed me huge respect. I had a service with Sister Maria; it meant everything. It was peaceful and calming.

I felt alone in my farewell to Grandad, and thought of all my family and friends who would be at his real service. I was also grateful for the condolences from some of the women.

As I headed back to the house, Mia came running towards me. 'Oh, Tilly, I'm so sorry. Are you alright?' She clasped her arms around me and held me tightly. I shrugged her off; I could tell she wasn't sincere. I thanked her but I wanted to spit. She wasn't the friend I thought she was.

August 1

The kids came to visit. It was a good day. *I love them so much – I'm so very proud of them.* Kate said Jake had booked to come and see me.

August 4

I got ready for a visit but was told there wasn't any booked. I tried ringing Jake but got no answer. *Why is he not coming?*

I waited anyway, in the hope he'd still come, but eventually had to concede that he'd let me down. *He's telling family he's visiting me but he's not!* I felt worthless, invisible, a nonentity. *Why do I love that piece of shit?*

August 10
Karen got her parole; she ran into work to tell us. *I'm so happy for her.*

August 12
Living with junkies was like living on a knife edge. The prisoners kept asking me to take a urine test for them. I was scared to say no - if I was found out I'd be in serious trouble. *Why can't they just leave me be?*

On Saturday, a girl from our house, who I didn't know well, had a visit from her mother. Apparently, when they kissed goodbye, it was on the lips, and the mother managed to pass a wrap of drugs into the girl's mouth. The girl later inserted them into her vagina - standard practice for prisoners in Style, as the guards were not allowed to give internal body searches.

Her mistake was to brag about the drugs when she got back to the house. I couldn't believe how quickly people moved. Four women got hold of her - they literally dragged her up the stairs into her bedroom. I was scared for the girl, so I followed them, shouting at them to stop. I could hear the poor girl screaming that she'd share the drugs.

I reached the bedroom door and saw them viciously rip off her trousers and knickers. She was then pushed onto the bottom bunk. Two women pinned her down, while another two took it in turns to 'de-crutch' her. This was done without any concern for the girl, who was screaming and kicking her legs to get the offenders off her. Her face was contorted in pain.

One of the women holding the girl down put a hand over her victim's face, to muffle her screams. She then screamed herself, as her hand was bitten; I saw blood coming from her hand. She punched the girl in the face in retaliation. I could only watch, too scared to stop the brutality.

They searched the girl's vagina, grabbing at anything to retrieve the drugs. One woman inserted her arm up the girl so far, I couldn't see her wrist.

I was sickened and saddened at what I'd witnessed. I turned and walked away slowly, tears clouding my vision. *This place is like a jungle.* People's behaviour, so depraved and desperate. *Even animals don't act that way.* I was utterly shocked at what humans could do to each other.

I stared out of the large window that overlooked the grounds. It was a sunny day, with a deep blue sky. The grass was iridescent, like an emerald carpet. A large oak tree stood majestically in the sunshine, its branches gently swaying with the breeze. On the other side of the glass was civilisation. I wanted to be back there. I couldn't block out the chaos and noise vibrating throughout the house.

I thought about my grandad and how I'd missed his funeral. A joke he used to tell jumped into my head. I could hear his voice putting on a funny German accent: 'Vat ist German for a bra?' He'd laugh and say, 'Dishill-stop-um-flappen.' I started laughing, remembering his wide smile when he told that joke. I laughed and laughed – in fact, I couldn't stop laughing.

Lisa approached. She sat down next to me at the top of the stairs. 'What's so funny?'

I couldn't reply in my mirth. She started to laugh with me, but after a few minutes my laughter turned into sobs. She put her arms around me and we sat there in silence.

August 15
I was called to the governor's office. I had no idea why. I secretly hoped I'd got a place at Askham, the

open prison that was much nearer home; I'd just applied for enhanced status. I wasn't aware I was in any trouble.

After breakfast, I headed to his office. When I got there, I found the governor chatting with a couple of guards as he stood next to his huge desk. The conversation stopped as soon as I entered the room.

The desk took up most of the room; it was beautifully carved, with intricate patterns on the legs. It looked as old as the building it was in. The governor moved behind the desk and indicated for me to sit down. I tentatively sat in the chair facing him, nervous about what he would say.

'McVeigh, I've called you in today, unfortunately, with bad news.' He looked straight at me.

'Oh God, what's happened?'

'Your mother's in hospital. She's had a heart attack. She's in intensive care. Don't worry, she's stable. We've made arrangements for you to visit her.'

I just stared at him. I felt tears in my eyes and he passed a couple of tissues across the desk. I dabbed my eyes and blew my nose. 'When can I see her?' I croaked.

He looked to the two officers at the back of the room. 'These officers will escort you. You can leave in an hour.' I jumped out of the chair and made for the door. He called me back. 'You'll have to complete a form before you go. Don't worry, we'll get you there soon.'

All I could think of was getting to my mother. I dashed to my room, changed into a decent outfit, and paced impatiently until I was collected.

The journey took about an hour. We travelled in a car, though I was still handcuffed and uncomfortable. One guard drove, the other sat in the back with me. They talked about football. I kept quiet, reminiscing about my life with Mum. I was scared to see her. *Was she going to survive? Had the death of my grandfather brought this on? Was I to blame?*

We arrived at Pinderfields Hospital. 'Please can you take off the cuffs?' I asked. 'I don't want my mother to see me in these.' After some discussion, they agreed to take them off, though they insisted that one of them held my arm. *What did he think I was going to do? Do a runner, when visiting my sick mother?*

We found the right ward. One guard stayed in the corridor, the other held on to me. I spotted Dad and went to him. The guard let go of me.

Laid in her hospital bed, my mother looked like a waxwork model. She had an oxygen mask covering her face and various tubes coming out of her arms. There was a loud beeping from the machine at her side. White pads, attached by wires, were on her chest, poking out from her nightie.

She was asleep, or at least, that's what I hoped. She looked frail. Dad was sat in the chair next to the bed; he looked tired. He got out of the chair and hugged me so tightly, I coughed and spluttered. I started crying. I felt so safe in his arms.

The officer pulled out a chair from the other side of the bed. 'You sit here, Tilly. I'll wait for you in the corridor.'

I was glad he'd left us alone, but the damage was already done. The cuffs may have been off, but he was in uniform – it wouldn't take a genius to realise I was a prisoner. Some of the visitors around other patients' beds stared over at me. I wiped the tears from my eyes and stared right back at one of them. She looked away quickly.

Dad rubbed my back gently. 'I didn't think they'd let you come. It's lovely to see you. You look thin...how are you?'

I couldn't reply; my words caught in my throat.

'Your mum's doing alright. They're going to move her to the cardiac ward. She's groggy, but okay.'

I gently put Mum's hand in mine. She opened her eyes and stared right at me, then shut them again. I kept hold of her hand and turned to Dad. 'When did this happen? I didn't know she was ill, not until this morning.'

He sat on the armrest of the chair and put his arm around me. 'It was out of the blue, her heart attack. She's doing well, she's in the right place. I'm glad you're here, even if it is for a short time. It'll mean a lot to your mum. I can tell you, it gave me a real scare, but the ambulance came quickly and she's going to be alright.'

He made the sign of the cross then went to the other side of the bed to hold Mum's other hand. He looked pale and much older than when I'd last seen him. He constantly turned his rosary beads in his other hand.

I leaned over and kissed Mum's head. She never moved and she felt clammy. I held on to her hand, squeezing it gently. I closed my eyes and recited the Lord's Prayer - Dad joined in. When I looked over at him, I felt an overwhelming rush of love. 'Keep strong, Dad. Mum needs you. I need you.'

Mum moved her hand from mine and placed it on her tummy. I was shocked that she was awake. She mumbled something and Dad leaned in closer. 'Yes, I know you're tired and you need your rest. Tilly will be leaving soon, but she wants to spend this time with you.'

I leaned closer, too. 'Get well soon, Mum. Dad needs you. And thank you for looking after Elliot and being there for us all. I'm so sorry about Grandad...I've written to Grandma. I appreciate everything, Mum. I love you, please get better.'

She kept her eyes closed but I noticed tears rolling down her cheeks. I gave her a hug. She flinched, so I let go and kissed the top of her head instead. I sat back down, full of shame.

Dad nattered on, updating me on changes and events in the lives of our family and neighbours. Half an hour later, the guard came over and said we had to leave.

On hearing the stranger's voice, Mum opened her eyes and looked right at me. I could physically feel the coldness of her stare. She didn't say anything and closed her eyes again.

I started to cry and took hold of her hand again. 'Mum, I'm sorry. I know I've shamed you, but please get better, that's all I ask.' She just laid there.

Dad put his arms around me. We hugged for a while then the guard took my arm and guided me out. My heart broke when I looked back over my shoulder to see Dad in tears.

Back in the car, the two guards carried on their boring conversation about football. I was handcuffed again; I leant my pounding head against the head-rest. I'd stopped crying but felt emotionally drained. I stared out of the window and thought of Mum. We'd always had a volatile relationship. Mum was a strong, feisty woman; Dad had often been forced to play peacemaker, especially when I was a teenager.

The whole time I was in prison, it was Dad who wrote letters to me. It was Dad who spoke to me when I rang their house. On the first few calls, I'd ask to speak to Mum. He'd come up with excuses as to why she couldn't come to the phone.

I got the message, eventually. I knew she was embarrassed and ashamed of me. And, after visiting her today, I was certain she'd never, ever forgive me.

I was shattered by the time we got back to Style. A

few nights after the hospital visit, I had a nightmare that came back again and again.

I was not one to have dreams or nightmares and it scared me, to a degree. I dreaded going to sleep most nights.

It always began in darkness. I could sense I was floating in water. It lapped, serenely, around me. The soft light turned blue, dappled with yellow sunbeams. The sensation was like the bobbing of a cork in liquid.

I could see the sky beyond the surface and the sun shining above. I was able to breathe but I couldn't move unless the water took me. The only sounds I could hear were the lapping of waves and my heavy breathing.

Sounds were amplified as I was suspended under-water. I'd see shapes drifting towards me. The water carried them nearer and nearer. I still couldn't move.

The shapes took the form of people. It dawned on me that these were my children drifting towards me, their arms reaching out. I'd try to raise my arms and catch them, and noticed their faces were full of alarm, as they bobbed around like ragdolls. Their hair splayed out above their heads, as if they were being dragged to the surface.

Suddenly, the water would turn cold, and its colour turned a murky grey. My children would drift past me. They'd open and close their mouths, as if they were trying to scream, 'Mum!'

Again, I'd try and raise my arms and move my legs, in a bid to swim to them - but they were always out of reach. Then they'd float backwards, out of vision. I'd scream, but no sound would come out.

There would just be absolute silence - a silence that made me believe I was dead.

I'd gasp when a deafening, almighty crashing of waves exploded in my ears. The noise distorted into a distant voice. I'd strain to hear what was said, and eventually, it became louder and clearer. It was always my mother's voice, shouting, 'You're no daughter of mine!'

At this point I'd always wake up, coughing from the drowning sensation. My heart would be pounding. Sobbing, and struggling to breathe, I'd feel helpless.

I couldn't save my children. And my mother has disowned me.

Chapter Twelve

By now, I'd been in prison almost a year. I thought I would be able to hack it, but lack of sleep and recent experiences had left me numb and lethargic. *What's the point in going on? No one's on my side, except my kids. And what effect is this having on them?* I felt so guilty, and frightened - living amongst evil, violent women. *Am I really the same as them?*

I seriously contemplated suicide, but couldn't go through with it. As I fought with my emotions week in, week out, Lisa proved a good friend. During my breakdown, she made sure I ate, and insisted I drank water as well as coffee. Every night she ran a bath for me, and even bathed me when I didn't have the energy to move. She put me to bed and talked to me before lock-up, sometimes into the night. She even washed my clothes.

I remember sharing my life story with her. Not just how I'd got there, but stories of happier, better times. I knew it was morally unforgivable to feel sorry for myself, without much thought to the victims of my crime, but it was hard to feel anything else in there. I just wanted my life back.

August 20
Mum was discharged, which made Dad very happy. Though I was glad she was better, she still wouldn't talk to me. Unsurprisingly, that made me sad.

August 23
Karen returned from a home visit and brought in some fresh yeast; her intention was to make 'hooch'. She couldn't stop laughing; she'd arrived at the house and walked straight in on Donna and Nicky having sex.

Sept 1

Maz was another inmate who shared her story, only it wasn't necessarily one we wanted to know. Apparently, she was an arsonist, and she openly admitted that she loved fire.

Lisa and I were in our room talking, about two hours before lock-up, when Maz came in. She seemed a little naïve, and the sort of person who tried to please others. It was as if she didn't have an original thought of her own and desperately wanted to be liked.

She was around twenty years of age, but looked much younger. She had short, black spiky hair, thick eyebrows, and big brown eyes with thick eyelashes. She was slim, of average height, but had large breasts, both of which she'd had tattooed - one with an angel, one with a devil.

The tattoo on her left upper arm interested me; it said, 'I love dogs'. As we chatted, I asked her about its meaning.

'What do you mean, what's its meaning?' she snapped. 'I love dogs. I like cats, too, but I prefer dogs.'

I blushed. 'Oh, I just thought it had an alternative meaning. I get it, I prefer dogs, too.'

Sept 4

I was told to ring Jake at his friend's house, but the phone was engaged all evening. I never got to speak to him that night. I desperately wanted to. *He's obviously out enjoying himself, and not bothered with me.* I felt tortured by his callousness.

Sept 14

Another visit from Kate and Elliot, which cheered me up no end. I could never get used to the surges of emotion, though. Excitement, as I counted down the hours until they came, enjoying their company whilst they were there; but I hated the feeling of loss when they left.

Kate was angry and upset about Jake not visiting me. 'He's so weak,' she said. 'And I'm concerned about Elliot.'

'What do you mean?'

'Jake drinks constantly.'

I tried to waylay her fears. 'Everything will be alright. The family are doing everything they can.' She sighed and looked at her coffee cup. 'Hey, perhaps we should do what the woman in the next house to me did with her husband.'

'Why, what did she do?' asked Kate.

'She cut him up and fed him to her ferrets.' Kate laughed.

Sept 19

It had been a long day. After work, in our room, Lisa and I offloaded our gripes.

Sick of moaning, and to change the subject, I turned to Maz. 'Why do you like to start fires?' I asked. 'What sort of buzz does it give you? Will you set fire to anything?'

Maz looked puzzled.

'We just wondered when your fascination with fire started,' said Lisa. 'Aren't you afraid of the flames? You could get hurt.'

Maz appeared to misinterpret our interest, as her face changed instantly. 'I'm going to get some water,' she said, and stormed out of the room.

Though it was clear we'd upset her, Lisa and I didn't think much more of it and continued to chat. Maz returned a few minutes later. She calmly walked to her bunk and flashed us a smile.

'So, what's your day been like, Maz?' asked Lisa.

'Okay, thanks,' she replied, smiling again. She had a weird expression on her face.

'I'm just going to the loo,' I said, 'won't be a minute.'

As I crossed the hallway I saw people running around. A voice from downstairs screamed, 'Fire!'

I ran to the bathroom, quickly used the toilet, and sped back into the bedroom. Maz was still on her bunk, smiling.

'We need to get out!' Lisa shouted frantically. Maz didn't move.

'Don't just sit there!' I screamed. 'There's a fire!' At that, she followed us down the stairs.

Guards were urgently shepherding everyone out of the building. When the firemen came, women shouted obscenities at them, and made lewd gestures.

I looked to the crowd and spotted Maz; she was still smiling. The fire was quickly put out - apparently, it had started in the television room. The curtains had been set alight. There wasn't too much damage done, and we were allowed back inside a few hours later.

Beforehand, however, the police interviewed everyone. Lisa and I had already agreed that we wouldn't say anything about our conversation, even though we both knew Maz had started the fire.

When questioned, I said that Maz had been in our room, and that I'd only left for a few minutes to go the toilet. Lisa said the same. We both felt like we'd played some part in it all, asking Maz about her fascination with fire. The last thing we wanted was to get her into trouble; her sentence would have been extended.

We were allowed a hot drink in the kitchen before lock-up. As everyone returned to the house, they talked about Maz, blaming her for the fire. Lisa and I kept telling them that Maz couldn't have started the fire, as she'd been with us the whole time.

For a few days afterwards, the girls picked on Maz and made her life a misery. *I'd hate to be bullied like that.*

Sept 27

We were introduced to a new roommate: Jannie. She was eight-and-a-half months pregnant, and very frightened. It was her first time inside.

You could never really relax with all the comings and goings of prison life. Joan was released – I'd had no idea she'd left until Jannie arrived. I'd not had much interaction with Joan, but it still felt weird that she was there one minute then gone the next.

Pauline seemed jittery at tea-time; I suspected she'd taken or injected something. We sat down to eat, and suddenly she leant over and grabbed my pork sausage. I was too astonished to react. She chewed the food as best she could with the teeth she had left. The sight sent me into hysterics.

Sept 28

Lisa got her probation. Those in house 'E' all wanted to be friends with me, now she wouldn't be there to carry out their fake tests. *I wish they'd leave me alone.*

One girl, a heroin user, told me she'd inserted a small plastic bottle in her vagina. She'd filled it with another girl's urine. The top was covered with cling-film, so if she went to the toilet, it wouldn't contaminate the other girl's sample. She walked round the whole day with that bottle inside her. She seemed to think she'd fooled the system and was very proud of the fact, despite her obvious discomfort.

Sept 29

Pandemonium struck. The word got out that drugs

were available. Women everywhere got high. I blocked out what was happening; I had to be positive and think good thoughts. I was starting to feel stronger, and more like my old self. The thought that I might get the 'enhanced status' I'd applied for became my focus. It would mean extra visits, more money and phone cards.

As I contemplated this in my room one day, Jannie came in. She was worried about giving birth, which was due to happen any day, and what would happen to the baby once he or she was born. Her life story was heartbreaking. Her husband was a lowlife - a heavy drinker who spent what money they had on booze. She was already mother to two children, and had resorted to stealing so she could feed them.

She'd been caught a couple of times by supermarket security, and received a caution. Eventually, she was charged and given a six-month prison sentence. Her children were put into care.

The mother and baby unit at Style was full, so she'd been placed within the general houses. She was in absolute turmoil, knowing that, as soon as she gave birth, her child would be taken from her. I was at a loss as to what I could say to help or comfort her. I really didn't know how she managed.

It was crystal clear that she loved her children. She didn't deserve the life, the husband, or the sentence she'd ended up with. Her predicament made me think of home; I was so grateful to God that my children were safe and secure.

Sept 30

Maz slit her wrists in the bathroom and was taken away. Lisa and I were extremely upset to hear the news.

Did we subconsciously encourage her to start that

fire? Were we responsible for everything she suffered afterwards? I couldn't sleep for worrying.

Oct 1

I argued with Jake, over nothing, really. I don't know why I kept putting myself through it. I'd ring home and we'd always end up shouting at each other. He was selfish, I could clearly see that, but the thing was, I didn't care anymore. He must have thought everything would be the same between us, but it couldn't be.

I was so angry that, when I was stopped on the way back to the house by another inmate, and asked if I'd fake a drugs test for her, I shouted, 'No!'

Oct 4

A new girl in the house: Debbie. I disliked her from the start. She looked to be around thirty years of age; she was taller than me, with wide shoulders, a thin waist and long legs. She had short, wavy hair that was dark brown with blonde highlights. She was certainly pretty, but her voice grated on me.

She talked through her nose and constantly chewed gum. She always stood with her arms across her chest, as if waiting for confrontation, whenever she spoke to someone. She was full of herself, and I found her cocky.

Oct 7

I received a letter from Jake. It was filled with love, and it warmed my heart to think that he still cared about me. I rang him but felt let down when I found he was drunk again. *It's getting boring now.* I had to end it, for Elliot's sake, as well as mine. He said he would visit so that we could talk.

Oct 8

I got ready for Jake's visit. He didn't show. *He lied to me again.* I wanted to say so much to him – about how he'd not been there for me. I'd begun to dislike him, and once I'd made up my mind, I knew I wouldn't go back. I'd learnt that he didn't care – I wasn't really sure he ever had. *I've been so stupid. I just wanted someone to look after me – why have I never found that?* Was I so worthless?

Oct 9

A few weeks had gone by since Karen brought in the yeast. Containers of brewing liquid had been hidden all over the house - under beds, in cupboards where the cleaning equipment was kept, under the kitchen sink, and the rest in various girls' lockers.

Karen kept her eye on everything and started to organise a 'house party'; as far as I was aware, not many people knew about it. Those that did swore to keep it secret. Excitement started to build.

Party night kicked off a couple of hours after lock-up. Karen distributed the fermented hooch to everyone holding out a cup. There was some scuffling and pushing, but the banter was friendly, which made a nice change. Three cheers all round.

I drank a few cups of the so-called ale. It tasted rancid, but it had the desired effect. It was unbelievably strong; it made your eyes water and your throat feel like it was on fire, but people drunk it regardless. I stood with Lisa and helped make sure everyone got a drink. When the container was empty, Lisa traipsed off to fetch more of the 'loony juice'.

The house became loud and raucous. I sat on the bottom step of the stairs with a small group of women. We became rowdier and rowdier as we belted out our favourite songs. 'Your voice is so loud, it's like a bloody foghorn!' one woman said to me.

'Well, if you're at sea and surrounded by fog, you know who to call,' I cackled. I then started to sing 'Popeye, the sailor-man'. Some of the girls joined in and my face ached from laughing so much.

The booze took hold. I felt liberated, and it was probably the first time I'd properly relaxed since incarceration. I wasn't a big drinker, and I soon became groggy, and started to slur my words.

I thoroughly enjoyed the sing-song until my voice gave way. I decided to go upstairs; it took me a few attempts to get up from the step. I clung to the balustrade to steady myself as I climbed the stairs. At that point, the party became one I no longer wanted to attend.

There were other women sat on the steps, and I had to negotiate my way round them. One of them - someone I'd always thought of as quiet and unassuming - thought it would be funny to give me a shove. I screamed as I lost my balance, but I managed to hold on. I eventually righted myself. 'You cretin, I could have broken something!' I snapped.

She stopped laughing to reply, 'Nah, you'd have bounced because you're pissed.'

I just ignored her. Further up the stairs, I passed a couple of girls having sex in front of everyone. I tried to keep my eyes fixed on the stairs.

Some women were openly taking drugs without a care in the world. I reached the top step and heard raised voices, as if a brawl had started. People rushed towards the fight, to either join in or stop it. I just wanted to lie down.

The shouting, screaming, singing and laughing whirled round the house into a tumultuous cacophony. At one point, I thought the roof would blow off. I hurried to the bathroom, desperately needing a wee. A girl darted ahead of me; I heard her vomiting.

After I'd used the loo I went into the bedroom and found Karen and Lisa huddled together on one of the bottom bunks. Karen looked upset. 'Are you alright?' I slurred.

She shook her head. 'It's all gone fucking wrong... it's bedlam out there. I'm right in the shit now. I'll lose my probation.' I'd never seen her look so scared. And I was shocked to realise this made me happy. *This loud mouth...frightened!*

I staggered over and tried my best to sound serious. 'It'll be alright - not many of the girls know who made the stuff. They're all drunk anyway...surely they won't grass you up?'

'You fucking idiot,' Lisa shouted at me in a flash of anger. 'It's just not this house that's got booze. Can't you hear next door?'

I staggered over to open the window. There was a commotion coming from the next house, and a riotous racket from every other building besides. The whole evening had turned into a riot. The atmosphere was electric, and quite frightening.

Already, I could see the night staff running from house to house. They tried to gain control by rounding up the inmates and locking each building. They sent for reinforcements.

I was upset that Karen hadn't confided in me, concerning the full extent of the 'party planning'. Neither had Lisa. *I thought they were my friends.*

I watched the mayhem from the window and lit a cigarette. Extra guards arrived. I turned to Karen and Lisa, and said, 'They think it's all over...it is now!'

I laughed at their worried faces, but inside I was seething that Lisa had shouted at me. I was going to make another remark, but stopped when guards stormed into the room. 'Move out!' one yelled. They were clearly not happy.

They herded us into the lounge for a head count. Nobody could stand up properly; women lurched and faltered, and had to hold onto furniture or lean against walls for support. One woman threw up, and a few others giggled like kids behind their hands.

By now, the guards had the police by their side. It didn't take long before they regained control.

During the night's activities, four women had beaten one of the guards - badly. They were sent to the segregation wing. We later learned that they'd all had time added to their sentences; they were also shipped off to other prisons. Luckily for Karen, no one mentioned how the hooch had been obtained. She was in the clear.

Oct 10

The next day, everyone was the worse for wear. People clutched their heads or groaned about the severity of their hangovers. The guards carried out a thorough search of all the houses, presumably to make sure the previous night was a one-off. No one had the energy to object and nothing untoward was found.

Oct 11

Following the party, I felt a change of vibe from Lisa. It wasn't that she was hostile, but she was definitely off-hand. She began to avoid me and she spent her time with the others. I had no idea why, or what I'd done.

One tea-time, she sat with Debbie and they laughed about a rumour they'd heard, about Mia giving a guard a blow job.

Mia had a job in the guard station, working in their kitchen. Rumours were always flying around concerning inmates and the guards. Mia had been seen with extra cigarettes, so she'd been asked what she'd done to get them.

'That Mia will go with anyone,' I heard Debbie say. 'She's always doing three-ways. She's just a filthy lesbian.'

Lisa turned to me with a sly grin on her face. 'Did you do blow jobs in Holloway, too, like Mia? Weren't you two mates in there?'

I continued to eat my tea and ignored her lewd remarks. Lisa persisted. 'The trouble with you, Tilly, is that you're too goody-goody. I bet you're even innocent of the crime you're in here for.'

I looked at her, bewildered. 'Why are you being like this, Lisa? What have I ever done to you?'

She laughed, and Debbie pretended to wipe her eyes. 'Ooh, what have I done? Poor me,' Debbie whined, 'stop picking on me.'

I tried to think of something clever to say. I looked at Debbie and saw her pick her nose. It was a disgusting habit at the best of times, but particularly when someone was eating. I didn't know if she was even aware that she did it. And she always had to look at what she'd extracted, and either flicked her findings from her finger or wiped it on her clothes.

'Do you have to do that while we're eating?' I said.

Debbie finished digging around and said, 'Who do you think you are, princess? I'll do what I fucking well like.' She then flicked her snot at me.

I thought I was going to be sick. I threw away what was left of my tea in the bin. 'You two seriously need to fucking grow up,' I said.

I felt like a caged animal, I was so angry. I wanted to walk off my frustration, or even run...I just wanted to get out. At home, if I ever felt angry, I'd just take Ellie, my dog, for a long walk. The tension would drain from my body. *I want to scream.*

Instead, I went to the bedroom and threw myself on

the mattress, crying. I wanted to hit something.

I laid there for a few minutes with my eyes closed, willing myself to calm down. I heard Lisa come into the room; she and Jannie whispered and laughed between themselves. I just ignored them.

Eventually, everyone came to bed. I vowed that I'd have it out with Lisa the following day, whatever the outcome.

Oct 12

I gazed out of the window; it had been a depressing day. The atmosphere in the house was stressed as routine drug tests were carried out. I noticed Jannie had gone; apparently, her waters had broken that morning.

I admired the seasonal scenery. It was a typical autumn day. The grass was covered with a thin layer of sparkling frost and the sky was a lovely bright blue. The trees had lost most of their leaves, which had resulted in a carpet of crisp foliage underneath. Gold, russet, browns and greens all sparkled in the soft sunlight. There was a constant rustling through the open pane from the leaves dancing in the cool breeze. I'd never really noticed my surroundings before prison – life always seemed to rush me here and there. With nothing but time to drink it all in, I was surprised how calm it made me feel.

Some hours later, Jannie arrived back at the house; she'd given birth and looked utterly exhausted. Her child had already been taken from her by social services. *How does anyone cope with that?*

I'd not had chance to talk to Lisa alone. I'd have to bide my time.

Oct 13

Karen went home. It felt sad to say goodbye, and to

someone I once thought of as a friend.

As some of us got dressed for breakfast, Jasmin, a girl from one of the other houses, came in. 'Lisa, put this stuff in your locker for me,' she said. 'We've heard our house is going to be swooped today.'

'Okay,' said Lisa casually. She took the bag Jasmin held out and put it in her locker.

'Don't bother looking in it,' warned Jasmin. 'Carol knows what's in there. I'll come and get it later.'

The others collected their clothes and walked out of the room. I hung around and waited for Jasmin to leave then shut the door, so that Lisa and I were alone. 'Why are you doing that?' I said. 'You're dicing with your probation. If that contraband is found, you'll have time added.'

She looked at me for a few moments. 'I don't want to wake up tomorrow and find I'm dead,' she said slowly, before laughing at what she'd said. 'Besides, it's none of your fucking business what I do.'

I must have looked shocked. Lisa sighed. 'Look, you know Jasmin is involved with Carol. Carol's a nut job - she practically runs this place. No one says no to Carol.' I paced the room. 'Take no notice of me,' she added softly. 'I'm just pissed off...I'm going through a bad patch. Finish getting dressed and let's go to breakfast. Don't worry about it.'

We went to breakfast, though I was anything but calm. Lisa was acting erratically. *Is it because Karen has gone, or is she doing drugs?* I watched her head off to her work; she looked miserable.

I had the morning to myself for a change; I was due to see the doctor in an hour and didn't have to go to work until the afternoon. I tried to read a book someone had lent me, but I wasn't really interested in it.

As I tried my best to concentrate a woman named Ann came in. She looked flushed and was out of breath. She said something quietly, which I didn't catch. 'What?' I said.

She came closer. 'They're going to swoop all the houses.'

I jumped off the bed. 'Are you sure?!' She nodded. 'For fuck's sake! Shit!' I said. 'I need to get to Lisa.' I set off running as fast as I could.

By the time I got to Lisa, I was out of breath myself. 'Give me your locker keys!' I screeched, as inconspicuously as I could.

'What are you on about?'

I wanted to scream at her, but I couldn't attract attention. 'Give me your keys...they're going to search our house.'

Her face fell. She quickly handed me the keys and I ran like the wind back to the house.

I went straight up to our room, relieved to see that the search had not yet started. I silently crossed my chest, thanking God for the opportunity. Without really thinking about my actions, I reached into the locker, grabbed the bag Jasmin had given Lisa, ran over to the window and tipped everything out onto the ground below.

I watched the stuff floating down; at that moment, I heard the guards enter the house. Sweat dripped down my back.

I saw a girl called Rachel hurriedly picking up all the tobacco, sweets, chocolate, foil wrappers and phone cards I'd chucked out the window. She was smiling, probably thinking her ship had come in as she picked up her spoils. She never once looked up to see who'd thrown the stuff out of the window. She just took off, running as fast as she could.

Later that afternoon, when calm had been restored, and nothing was found in our house, Lisa thanked me for my quick thinking.

I could tell she was worried about Carol, and the repercussions of the day's events. I was more than worried. I knew Carol would exert some payback for the things she'd lost.

That night, before lock-up, I approached Rachel. I pleaded for her to give back the stuff she'd collected. 'What do you mean?' she said. 'It wasn't me.'

Despite her defence, I could tell she was scared. 'Rachel, you do know who that stuff belonged to, don't you?' She didn't react. 'It's Carol's stuff.'

Her faced paled. 'I don't know anyone called Carol,' she said.

'You will,' I said. I tried to walk away with confidence, but my insides were churning.

Chapter Thirteen

In the sewing room, the following day, I approached Carol. I knew I only had a few minutes while the guard went to the toilet. I was shaking, but I had to make amends.

Carol was at her machine, talking to Jasmin. If they turned violent, I knew I'd have no chance. I tried to calm my voice. 'Carol, you don't know me. I'm Tilly. I'm in the same house as Lisa.'

Carol stood up and started to walk towards me. I tried to stand firm, and not look as frightened as the butterflies in my stomach made me feel. Two girls got up. She turned to them and said, with authority, 'No! It's alright, you stay where you are.'

She brought her attention back to me. 'What do you want?' Her voice was stern.

I swallowed. 'I threw your stuff out of the window, so the guards wouldn't find it. I was protecting Lisa... she could have lost her probation. I know who picked up your stuff. I've asked her to return it to you.'

She smiled at me. It wasn't a warm smile, it was menacing. 'I don't know what you're on about.' She walked back to her pals and sat down.

What do I do now?! If I turn round will they jump on me? I walked back to my machine quickly and, as I did so, the guard came back. I wasn't sure what had happened. *Was that the end of it?* Time at work that day seemed to drag more than usual.

I tried to concentrate on the sewing, but my mind was going round in circles. I'd put myself in this position to help a friend. *Am I going to be beaten up at some point in the future? Is Carol not going to do anything? Is she toying with me?* The not knowing was excruciating.

Rachel came to see me the next night. 'Thanks,

Tilly, I didn't know Carol, but I've asked around and have now returned everything to her.'

I hugged her tightly – I was almost in tears. 'Thank you, Rachel. Oh, thank God. I was going mad, wondering what to do. Thank you so much.'

The relief that flowed through my body was better than any emotion I'd ever experienced. I was glad to be alive, and thankful that I wouldn't need to look over my shoulder for the rest of my life.

Oct 16

Pauline gave up the drugs. She went cold turkey, but sadly, didn't cope well. She was marched to segregation after spitting at, and punching, a guard. I wasn't sure I'd cope any better in her situation.

She'd recently divulged that she'd been charged for aiding and abetting manslaughter. I was dumbstruck as she relayed the details.

Pauline and her partner had lived in a dingy squat that was used by several people who were also on drugs. People constantly came and went. Pauline admitted that, most of the time, she was 'out of it'.

Someone new arrived, who brought with them a seven year-old boy. That innocent child was subjected to beatings, and to being injected with God knows what, for a period of four days. No one helped him, and he tragically died. Pauline was sentenced to four years; her partner, twenty years.

I heard a similar story about a girl in another house. She and her partner had been 'shooting up' in their bathroom at home. She had two children, and one of them had disturbed the couple during their 'dig'. Both children were beaten to death.

I often prayed, after hearing such sorrowful life stories. I'd weep, overwhelmed by my guilt. *I'd tried to bring that poison into the country for money.*

Oct 17

It was a miserable day. It rained constantly, and it was bitterly cold. I had to make do with toast for breakfast; someone had nicked my cornflakes. I was cold, hungry, and very lonely.

After breakfast, I went through a risk assessment with the probation officer, where I completed various forms and we discussed how likely it would be that I'd abscond if let out of prison for home visits. We talked about the time I'd already served, and how I interacted with other prisoners. I saw what the officer wrote on my report: *Tilly does not make trouble; she helps other prisoners and is a hard worker.* Yet it stressed that I was a '*risk taker*'.

Returning to the house, after a very boring day at work, I was shocked to learn that Lisa had put in a request to change houses. I only found out when a new girl came into our room. I knew Lisa had a home visit coming up; I desperately wanted to talk to her before she left. I still didn't understand what her problem was with me.

Oct 18

At lunchtime, I searched for Lisa. I spotted her outside her new house, taking in the surrounding landscape.

'Admiring the view?' I said.

Lisa smiled. 'Hi, Tilly. What you up to?'

I lit a cigarette and stood next to her, enjoying the same view. Neither of us made eye contact. 'Lisa, what's your problem with me?' I blurted out.

She sighed heavily. 'I don't have a problem with you. I'm in a bad place at the moment. Because I'm going home soon, I'm finding it difficult to be here. I can't wait for my home visit, but the thought of having to come back here sucks. I know I get angry...and bitchy. This place affects you like that.' She paused. 'I don't know what I'm going to do, in the real world. I'm worried about Stefan. I know he's waited for me, but people change in here. You know that yourself.'

'I understand,' I said. 'Though I've been quite hurt by how you've been towards me.'

'Tilly, you really need to harden up a bit. I've been a good friend to you - especially during your breakdown. Just ignore me if I get tetchy.'

'So we're alright? There's nothing's wrong between us? You were just being a grumpy bitch?'

She looked me in the eye. 'Yes, that's about it.'

I gave her a hug. 'So, what made you move house?'

'Oh, I don't know...' she trailed off. 'After Karen left, I found it difficult to deal with my emotions. I hate saying goodbye to friends I've made inside.'

She sounded genuine enough, but my instincts, my inner voice, were screaming that something was off. I had no reason to doubt her. *Was I jealous, or just being paranoid?*

Oct 19

The family came to visit. Elliot looked to have grown a whole foot since I'd last seen him. *He's growing up too fast.* Kate said she'd got a new boyfriend. She seemed so happy. Jake was a no-show. *What's new?!*

I tried my hardest to show I was coping in front of the kids. Kate radiated a certain glow - the one that always spills out when you're in love. 'Tell me all about him,' I said.

She giggled, and gushed about how handsome he was. She described their first date, and how well he treated her. 'He's an electrician,' she said.

'That'll be handy,' I replied. Their relationship was going so well that, the following week, she was going to meet his parents. I felt anxious...she sounded so serious about this man, yet I'd never met him. I was so happy for her, though regret over the situation made my heart feel heavy.

I turned to Elliot. 'And how's school?'

He beamed. 'I've been chosen for the school football team!'

'How will you get to matches?'

'Grandad will take me, of course.'

I rolled my eyes at Kate. 'Of course...' I muttered.

I rang Jake after tea. He was drunk, as usual. I contained my frustration. 'Hi, Jake. How are you? I've had a lovely time with Elliot today – he's growing up so fast.'

'Don't give me a hard time, Tilly, I'm busy trying to stop the house from being repossessed. The bank has sent a letter, with a date for repossession.'

I gritted my teeth. 'Why have you not told me before? I thought it was all sorted. When do you have to pay by? And why have you not spoken to me about this before? This is important.'

His voice turned angry. 'What are you going to do about it from prison? You nag enough as it is. When you ring, you just ask about Elliot, or complain about how you're being treated inside.' He sighed. 'What can I do?'

'Stop getting pissed all the time and sort it out,' I shouted down the phone.

I heard the dial tone. I tried to call again but he must have left the phone off the hook.

Oct 20

The only thing that got me through the long days was the thought of a transfer to an open prison.

I gave a girl called Deb a haircut, but apparently, this made Nicky, another hairdresser, jealous. *What a sad place.*

Nov 1

Before breakfast, Lisa asked if she could borrow my white t-shirt. 'All my good clothes are packed for my home visit, and my brother's visiting today,' she said.

I was busy gathering my soap, toothbrush and towel for the bathroom, so I just handed her my locker key. 'Get it out while I go to the loo and get washed.'

When I came back, I saw that Lisa had emptied all my stuff onto a bunk. She was sat amongst my belongings, reading my diary. 'Hey!' I yelled. 'What the hell are you doing?'

'Just seeing if you've written anything about me. It's very interesting, this read.'

I snatched the diary from her. 'It's none of your business what's in here, you nosey cow! It's private!'

She stood up. 'Calm down. I've not read much, okay? Sorry. Look, I'll put everything back.' She began to shove my things back in their bag. 'Christ...why don't you put all this stuff in your drawers instead of this one bag? It must take you ages to find something.'

I started to cry. 'Because...this is not home. I will not treat it as home. I'll unpack my things when I get home, not before.'

She looked at me like I was mad. 'You're in denial, Tilly. Make life easier for yourself.'

I grabbed the bag from her. 'For God's sake, you're going soon. Don't lecture me on how to cope in here.'

She put her arm on my shoulder and spoke quietly. 'I'm sorry I've upset you. Thanks for lending me the t-shirt. I'll return it later today, unless you want me to send it to the laundry.'

I put the bag back into my locker. 'Just give it back when you've finished with it.'

She handed back the key. 'It won't be long before you're home, too. Just do your time and keep smiling.'

I spent the next hour smarting at her last remark. *Had she read that my house could be repossessed? Why am I second guessing everything she says?* I couldn't explain it, I just kept getting the feeling that something was wrong.

Nov 2

My dad came to see me for the first time. I noticed how worn out he looked as he struggled out of his overcoat. He was dressed in his best suit.

He gathered me in his arms and gave me a big hug. 'The drive down wasn't too bad,' he said. 'You look okay...are you coping alright?'

I started to cry. For a few minutes, all I could do was hold his hand. Eventually, I said, 'It's so good to see you. How is everybody? Have you seen Jake? It drives me crazy that I can't speak to you all whenever I want.'

'I've brought some good news, Tilly.' He squeezed my hand. 'Jake came to see me...he was in a right pickle. He told me his problems, and we came up with a solution. You're not going to lose the house!'

I opened my mouth and closed it again; no words would come out. He laughed. 'Your grandad left me and your mother some money. We talked about it, and, well, we're able to settle your debt.'

He waited for me to process what he'd said. I looked down at the table - my tears were bouncing off the surface. It was quite a while before I spoke. 'Dad, I can't expect you to do that. It's not fair on you and Mum. It's your money.'

He held my hand tighter. 'You're in a big enough mess as it is. I want to help. So does your mother. We went to a solicitor and Jake signed a document. He signed it on your behalf; it says that he'll pay us back each month. It means you can keep the house, and it stops further debt and higher interest if we do it this way. We expect the money back, at some point, mind, but at least you'll avoid repossession and all the stress that would have come with that.'

I looked him in the eye and solemnly promised to pay him back. 'You're so good to me. I'll do everything I can to repay you and Mum when I get out of here.'

I started crying again and even Dad had tears in his eyes. 'I know you will. You're all we have, Tilly – we're glad to help. Just promise that you'll never do anything like this again. I don't think me, or your mother, could take it.'

A pang of guilt shot straight through me. 'Dad, I promise. I'll shout it from the rooftops if it'll make you believe me. I'll never, ever do anything like that again. I'd rather die than come back here.'

When Dad had gone, I felt a mixture of sadness, exhilaration and overwhelming shame. Here I was, a grown woman, a mother-of-three, taking money from my elderly parents. *I'm such a disappointment...a convicted criminal, who has brought her family stress and heartache none of them deserved.*

Despite the disgust I held for myself and my actions, my heart also sang with joy. *My house is safe! Which means Elliot will be safe.* My relief was almost tangible.

Nov 5

In the distance I could hear bangs and whistles. Through the window I watched fireworks light up the sky.

I remembered how Guy Fawkes' night was always a big deal in our family. My mother's speciality was homemade treacle toffee, and my grandmother baked her delicious parkin. Dad lit the fireworks, and I'd sort the baked potatoes. I had wonderful memories of the

kids' faces as they made patterns in the air with spar-
klers. *Will I be out for Bonfire Night next year?*

Nov 10

Lisa came back from her home visit. I hadn't been
well; I was full of cold and I'd started having panic
attacks. *Life in here is doing me in.*

Lisa looked stunning in a brand-new outfit that
looked expensive. It comprised of a navy-blue skirt
and jacket. The jacket bore a white trim across the
lapel and collar. The pencil skirt was knee length; it
fitted her beautifully.

Under her jacket, she wore a powder-blue blouse
that had a V-shaped ruched detail. It was low cut and
subtly showed off her cleavage. On her feet were blue
mid-heeled court shoes, which perfectly complimented
the ensemble. She oozed class.

During her time on the outside, she'd visited a hairdresser; her highlights shone in the light, giving her
complexion a healthy glow. She looked good, but she'd
brought an attitude back with her. She smugly prattled on about her fantastic shopping trip, her colour
consultation, and how much everything cost. She'd
met up with Stephan, as well as family and friends;
they'd all enjoyed a banquet in a flashy bistro, feast-
ing on sumptuous food. I admit that I was consumed
with envy. I yearned for a similar experience.

Miserably, I looked at the clothes I had on. Tatty old
jeans, discoloured trainers. A t-shirt that had lost its
shape and was now much too big for me; the colour
had faded, after being washed numerous times by
industrial machines.

My hair was an absolute mess. I used to spend ages
titivating my hair when I had my salon - now I looked
and felt like a bag lady.

Lisa went into detail about her shenanigans on

the outside. How the meal with friends had lasted over two hours.

She'd sneaked a small glass of wine, not daring to have any more in case she was tested when she came back to prison. The vintage wine, apparently, cost £80 per bottle. As she described her dessert, our mouths started to water; her chocolate bombe sounded heavenly. A sphere of milk chocolate, filled with an orange-flavoured liqueur - the whole thing smothered with hot, dark chocolate, which made the sphere melt. It was served with cold vanilla ice-cream. One girl had tears in her eyes, she missed chocolate that much.

Lisa also bragged about how much sex she'd had during her visit. 'I'm red raw!' The girls raucously 'hoorayed' at that. 'But I've also come back with piles, because of all the rich food I've eaten,' she added.

Poetic justice.

When she'd finished regaling us with her tales and everyone had dispersed, she came over and hugged me. 'Oh, I've missed you,' she said.

I still couldn't put my finger on why I thought so, but she wasn't being sincere. It was as if she was on stage, playing a character, rather than being herself.

Nov 13

When I rang home, I heard an unfamiliar female voice in the background.

Elliot had answered, and we'd chatted for some time, then I heard a female shout, 'Tea's ready!'

'Who's there?' I asked.

'It's Carol. She's Daddy's friend,' said Elliot, innocently. 'She's making my favourite: fish fingers and chips.'

I was about to reply when Jake came on the phone. 'Hi Tilly,' he started, but I interrupted before he could say anything else.

'Who's there, Jake? You've got another woman in our house? You're unbelievable...and with our son there, too.'

I was ready to say more, but he shouted over me. 'Slow down a minute! You're jumping to conclusions.'

'Yeah, right.'

'Carol is Paul's girlfriend. She's here to help, that's all. Don't get any stupid ideas.' He sounded defensive.

'Okay. Put Paul on the phone then.'

Jake went silent for a minute. 'Paul's nipped to the shop, he'll be back soon,' he mumbled.

'Very convenient.'

'Look, we're just having some tea together. That's all.'

'You expect me to believe that, do you? Christ...' I started to cry. 'You bastard! Having a woman in my house. The house MY father helped to save. How could you?!'

'Stop! Please. Look, I'm visiting on the nineteenth. We can discuss it then.' He added, 'I'm going now. There's nothing going on, I promise.'

The dial tone buzzed in my ear. *He's lying, I know it.* I cried and cried that night. *Why am I surrounded by people who want to betray me? I know I've done wrong, but am I jinxed?*

Nov 18

I found it increasingly difficult to concentrate on anything. I kept thinking of Jake and that Carol woman. I couldn't sleep, and dreaded what the next day had in store.

Nov 19

For the first time, I didn't want Jake to visit. When he and Elliot arrived, I didn't let what had happened spoil the joy I felt at seeing my boy. I just scowled at

Jake - I don't know if he could tell that I was spoiling for an argument.

I noticed he looked red-eyed and tired. He held out his arms to give me a hug, but I backed away. I hugged Elliot, though, then sat down. 'How was the bonfire at Grandad's?' I asked.

'It was fab!' gushed Elliot. 'But Ellie was a bit scared of all the noises. Grandma put her bedding in the kitchen cupboard under the stairs, so she curled up in the dark out of the way.' He chattered on, 'She was fine the next day, but she found some of my treacle toffee. You should have seen her, Mum...she kept putting her paw up to her teeth because they were stuck together! I had to help her get it off.' He laughed at the memory.

Jake just sat there. 'Please can I have some money for the machine, Dad?' Jake handed over some change and waited until Elliot got up to make his choices.

He then turned to me. 'So, have you calmed down now? There was nothing going on. Carol came over with Paul, and he went to get some cigarettes from the shop. That's all.'

I tried to keep the sarcasm from my voice. 'I don't know any Paul or Carol...who are they?' I could tell he was annoyed.

'Paul's a friend I know through Tony, and Carol is his girlfriend.'

'And this Carol was making tea... She sounds very domesticated.'

In a flash of anger, Jake snapped, 'I was making tea. She just happened to turn up and help out.'

I'd known him long enough – I knew he was lying. My stomach started to churn. 'For how long has she been 'helping out', Jake? What was that term you used when I rang you that time...oh, yes, I'm getting 'too needy'. Who's needy now, if you can't cope and have to have women coming into our house to 'help out'?'

Jake shuffled in his seat. 'Stop it. Elliot's coming back.'

As Elliot munched his bag of crisps, I tried to concentrate on him. I asked how school was going, and what he'd done with his friends, completely ignoring Jake.

Before long, it was just ten minutes until visiting time finished. Jake had gone to the toilet. 'When Daddy's friend, Carol, came the other night, who else came to the house?' I asked Elliot. 'Was Kate there?'

I felt awful asking him such questions. Elliot scrunched his face up as he tried to remember. 'No, Kate wasn't there. Some man called in and talked to Dad for a bit. I took Ellie for her walk, and when I came back, the man had gone and Carol came in. She made tea.'

I spotted Jake coming back. 'Did Carol stay a long time?' I asked quickly.

'I don't know. After tea, I did my homework, then I got ready for bed.' I patted his hand.

Jake sat down. I changed the subject. 'So, how's work, Jake? Things must be easier, now Dad has paid off the house.'

Before Jake could reply, Elliot butted in. 'Oh, I remember... I went downstairs to let Ellie out, last thing, and saw Daddy kissing Carol as she was leaving.' He looked at me, then Jake.

Jake looked like he'd been poked with a red-hot cattle-prod. 'No, Elliot,' he said nervously. 'I didn't kiss Carol - I just gave her a peck on the cheek. That's what friends do.' He glared at me. 'What are you doing, putting Elliot in this position?'

I tried to smile, but inside I was dying. 'Because, Jake, Elliot doesn't lie to me.'

'Before you get on at me, it's YOU who's split this family up, bringing those drugs in. It's your fault you're not at home!'

I could tell Jake wanted to say more. Rage consuming me, I jumped up and grabbed at his face, digging my nails into both his cheeks. 'You lying, cheating bastard!' I screamed. 'I hate you! I fucking hate you! It's because of your gambling that I did what I did. You useless twat. YOU got us into debt. You've fucking wrecked my life! I'm in here because of YOU!'

Jake grabbed my wrists and yanked my arms forward as he stood up. I raised my right leg with the intention of kicking him in the groin. He must have realised what I was about to do; he pulled my arms down harder, until they were almost at my knees, and shuffled backwards. My knee missed its target, but my leg was free to kick out, and I forcefully jabbed at his legs with my foot again and again. Finally, I stamped on his left foot. He let go of my arms and hopped backwards, knocking over his chair.

I rushed at him again with my fists clenched and swung at his face. He put his arms up as a shield. I punched him a few times, but my blows just landed on his arms. I grabbed his shirt and pulled with all my strength. Buttons flew off as the material ripped.

I went to kick him again, but was snatched from behind. A guard twisted my right arm behind me, which brought me to my knees.

I started to sweat profusely and sobbed my heart out. 'Bastard!' I screamed again. 'This is all your fault...all your fault!'

The guard put his head to my ear. 'McVeigh! Shut up, and calm down!'

My heart was racing so fast, I thought my head would explode. My blood felt like it was boiling as it coursed through my veins. I became aware that the whole room had gone quiet. There wasn't a sound other than my cries and gasps for breath.

Elliot! My God, Elliot...

I looked up to see him crying and shaking. His hands were clasped, as if in prayer. I'd never seen him look so frightened. I tried to stand, but the guard wouldn't let me. 'Please let me up...I need to see to Elliot.' The guard ignored me and put cuffs on my wrists. He unceremoniously lifted me into a standing position by my armpits.

I watched Jake, who was only concerned with his shirt. The vain miscreant never once looked at Elliot.

I scanned the room. Prisoners and their visitors were gawping at us. Some were talking, others were laughing at the sad scene we'd played out.

Elliot ran to me, crying. He wrapped his arms around my waist and squeezed me tightly. His sobbing broke me inside. He clung on, and I dropped my head to kiss him.

I tried to sound calm. 'I'm sorry you saw that...it'll be okay, I promise. You'll be alright, Daddy will look after you. Mummy's just upset with Daddy, that's all. I lost control... You have to forget what you saw. It doesn't matter. It will never, ever happen again.'

In-between sobs, he whispered, 'Is it because of what I said about Daddy kissing Carol? Is it my fault?'

'No, Elliot. No, not at all. None of this is your fault.' As I said this, I glanced at Jake. He just looked shocked. I turned back to Elliot. 'I shouldn't have lost my temper. Honestly, Elliot, everything will be alright.' Eventually, he stopped crying, but he wouldn't let me go.

The guard told Jake to take Elliot out. As Jake reached for his son, he rubbed his cheek where I'd drawn blood. He wouldn't look at me.

He gingerly prised Elliot's arms from my waist.

'Come on, buddy, we're all upset. Your mum has to go now...so do we. You can come back soon to see Mummy.'

I kissed Elliot as he relaxed his grasp. 'You'll be fine, I'm alright.' As they walked away, Elliot turned and waved, his face crestfallen. 'I'm okay, you'll be alright. I love you,' I shouted. Jake just carried on.

The guard walked me out of the room. 'That was bloody stupid, in front of your son.'

I nodded. He was right. I was exhausted, the adrenaline fuelling my attack had now waned. It unnerved me to think how vicious I'd been. But it also cut me like a knife to think of Jake with another woman.

Why did I put my faith in such a loser? After all my family had done...he was such a selfish bastard. I felt disgusted, and there was a huge sense of loss within me, for who I'd thought of as the love of my life.

On top of all that, I was deeply ashamed that my son had seen me react in such a manner.

Chapter Fourteen

Nov 21

I was told to go to the governor's office after breakfast. I prayed it wasn't bad news about my mother. Once again, I sat at the ornate desk.

The governor appeared annoyed. 'McVeigh, you've been reported, because of your outburst at visiting time the other day.' He cleared his throat. 'I have to say, I'm very disappointed. We've also received some disturbing news about you.'

I stared at him blankly. 'What do you mean? Is my mother okay?'

He looked puzzled. 'As far as I'm aware, your family is fine. This is about you and your partner.' He shuffled some papers on the desk. Looking at them, rather than me, he said, 'I've been informed that you funded the purchase of your house from the proceeds of drugs. And not only that, you're friends with a known drug baron. I can only conclude that you're more heavily involved with drugs than it appeared at the time of your arrest.'

I didn't know how to respond to such preposterous allegations. After a long pause, I said, 'Governor, I'm sure you're aware that when I was arrested, my house was searched. My finances were investigated, as were my partner's. It was proven that we had no money. That's why I'm in prison...I committed the crime of smuggling drugs to get some money.'

The governor remained silent, which made me more nervous, and I started to babble. 'It was stupid of me...but I was desperate, because we were going to lose the house. And I'm sorry for the outburst at visiting time. It won't happen again.'

He changed tack. 'How do you know Dan Saunders? He's notorious, and well-known for drug importation, and possibly murder. We know he's involved with other illegal activities; it's just a matter of time before he's caught and incarcerated.' He tapped the end of his pen against the desk with every syllable. 'If you're in league with such a person, it does not bode well on you, McVeigh.'

I was amazed at how angry he sounded. 'I don't know Dan Saunders! I've only ever met him once. It was at York races...at a social event. I met many people that day. I was introduced to him, and we chatted about horses, then he was gone. I had no idea he was a criminal.'

My heart was racing, and I took in a long breath. 'I have no contact with this person, Governor,' I said firmly. 'And I'd like to know who told you that I'm supposedly involved with him.'

He ignored my question. 'I'm afraid I have no choice but to send you back to main prison. I don't like this outcome. I know you've been a model prisoner here, but these allegations will have to be investigated. I certainly do not want any trouble at Style. In the meantime, as procedure dictates, you'll be transferred to Newhall in a couple of days. That is all.'

I was in total shock as the guard escorted me back. *Where the hell is all this coming from? Who's saying this about me?* My world felt as if it had finally bottomed out. I wasn't sure I could cope with main prison again. I had to think.

Nov 23

Everything became a blur during the days that followed. Eventually, I was taken to Newhall, and stood, waiting to be processed, in the prison's reception.

I did what was asked of me; I was terrified. The guards there were intimidating and unapproachable. There was just one good point – I was nearer home;

therefore, visits wouldn't be such a slog for my family. *I hope I can hack this.* I became anxious when they locked me in. The inmates seemed aggressive and hardened. My mind turned over and over...*who's been spreading rumours about me? Someone put me in here, but who?*

I realised I hadn't said goodbye to Lisa.

Nov 25

I applied for a job in the kitchen. I hoped it would motivate me, as I did nothing but sleep all the time, I was so depressed.

I received a letter from Kate; she and Elliot were going to visit in a couple of days. My head was battered, I couldn't concentrate.

Nov 27

Kate came, but I couldn't see her because the prison was in lock-down. Apparently, an inmate had visited the dentist and pinched some apparatus.

Everyone was locked in their cells for the morning. Each cell was searched. Some of the girls managed to find out who the culprit was, and it was rumoured that she'd receive a beating when the opportunity arose. I was put on an 'offender behaviour course'.

Dec 1

I started work in the kitchen. I shared a cell with a woman called Denise, a Liverpudlian.

The long hours actually helped, as I still couldn't think straight. My thoughts jumped between Jake and Lisa. *Did Lisa tell those lies about me?* Jake was just a bastard, full-stop, in my eyes.

Dec 20

Kate's visiting tomorrow, I've got to get better. I had

flu, as well as suffering an extremely heavy period. I couldn't stop bleeding; the stomach pains were excruciating. Most prisoners were depressed as Christmas approached.

Dec 21

I'd found out that Denise was due to go home in a few days. I worried who would be put in with me when she went.

Kate, Elliot and Dad came. Visiting time seemed to go much faster than usual. Kate was a little stressed; she was going to help my mother cook Christmas lunch. Her boyfriend was going to join them. She was still very happy with him.

Dad looked well. He said that Mum was also in good health. Elliot was buzzing about what he was going to get for Christmas - he kept reeling off his Christmas list to anyone who'd listen.

Kate asked Dad to take Elliot for a drink of pop, so she could talk to me alone. She seemed troubled. 'There's no easy way to say this, Mum, so I'll just say it. Jake's seeing someone. I found out through Elliot, he kept mentioning this Carol.'

I nodded for her to continue.

'I've talked it over with Grandad and we thought it was better coming from me.' She took a deep breath. 'I called at the house a few nights ago and saw her myself. She's been picking Elliot up from school and making his tea.'

'Is she staying at the house...sleeping with Jake while Elliot's there?' I tried my best to keep my anger in check. It wasn't Kate's fault.

'No. Monday to Friday she doesn't stay. When Elliot goes to Grandad's for the weekend, though, who knows? I think Jake stays at her house.'

'Well, that's a blessing,' I said sarcastically.

Kate chewed her bottom lip. 'Look, I know you won't want to hear this, but she's quite nice. And if it wasn't her, it would be somebody else. Jake can't cope on his own. I'm not saying it's right, but at least she's helping Elliot. Jake's aware we all know. He'll stay in the house with Elliot and move out when you're released. He's going to write to you soon.'

I put my head in my hands and tried not to cry. *I don't want to cry all the time.* 'Okay. Elliot will be spending most of Christmas with Dad anyway, and Mum will spoil him. I've a lot to be grateful for.'

Despite my apparent positivity, I started to shake. I was upset and angry, not just with Jake, but at myself for putting my faith in him.

I was still processing what Kate had said when Dad sauntered back to the table. I was sad when they left, but also relieved. I needed to lay down, I was exhausted.

Dec 26

Christmas Day, unsurprisingly, was a sombre affair. A few prisoners sung carols. The food was better than normal.

I'd phoned to wish everyone a Merry Christmas. I still hadn't received a letter from Jake. I needed to blank him from my mind. I had no life in me at all.

Denise was going - and another woman, Linda, who I'd got to know. Everyone seemed to go before me. I should have been able to cope – I'd served such a long time, but I felt weaker as each day passed. I felt as if I was going to die.

Dec 31

It was a bad day in the kitchen. There was a horrible atmosphere as two people were sacked. I didn't care anymore; I felt that prison was changing me into something I didn't want to be. *I can't stand it any more...*

Jan 9

I thought a change of routine would pull me out of my mental abyss, so I applied for a job on the farm – the fresh air would help blow the cobwebs from my mind.

I tried to pull myself together, but then I'd wallow in self-pity, anger, guilt and shame. My mind was all over the place. *I have to get stronger and sort myself out. No one will do it for me.* Jake wasn't going to be there for me, that was clear. I had to face my future alone. At least I had my family – they'd always be there for me, they'd proved that. No matter what.

I was lonely after Denise left. I looked forward to being on the farm; I just hoped it would lift my spirits. I didn't mind hard work.

I did my risk assessment and was told the conditions for opening and closing the gate. Time dragged on. I applied for enhanced status, too, hoping my luck would turn. I needed something to look forward to.

Jan 16

I was moved onto the enhanced wing. *I've got a television!* The wing felt less stressful and violent than the one I'd come from.

I chatted to a girl who'd been there eight years - since she was seventeen years-old. Her first chance of parole was years away. I realised that I had to be grateful; some people had it much worse.

Jan 20

Mrs. Hill, my probation officer, completed my transfer application. It was for Askham, an open prison just around the corner from my home.

She also completed a resettlement leave form; in

March or April, I could start home visits.

I was on top of the moon and felt ten years younger. I desperately wanted to stay positive. *Things can only get better. Thank you, God.*

Jan 24

Dad, Kate, James and Elliot visited. Mum didn't come, but at least she was well. The time always flew by when my loved ones came, yet the minutes and hours dragged after they'd gone. The drudgery brought enough misery.

They'd all been happy about my possible home visits, and the better conditions I'd enjoy, if my transfer to Askham was approved. 'You look so much better, Tilly,' said Dad, as he hugged me goodbye. 'You don't look as drawn as you did.' *Because I have hope again.*

Jan 25

I was still on a high from the family's visit. I rang home, and was shocked when Dad answered. 'Hi, Tilly, what have you been up to?'

'What do you mean?'

'I had a phone call this morning, then a visit from one of your prison friends.'

'What? Who? I don't understand.'

'Her name was Lisa.'

It felt like a claxon had gone off in my head.

'She rang here,' he continued, 'talking about how you owe money to someone in prison. She volunteered to call here and collect it, then she can pass it on to you.'

I was so shocked, I couldn't speak.

'So...I gave her directions and she called this afternoon. She seemed nice, Tilly. Very educated. She was smartly dressed when she came - your mother gave her tea and biscuits.'

'Don't tell me you gave her money,' I whispered.

'Yes, I gave her £100. She's going to give you it when she gets back to prison.'

'Oh my God, Dad...Lisa left prison ages ago. And she was in Style with me, not Newhall. That bitch has conned you. I can't believe this. I don't know how she got your number.'

Then a thought came to me. 'That bitch. That bloody bitch! It was her...she told the governor...'

Dad tried to interrupt but I talked over him. 'What did she say the money was for? Think!'

I could hear him talking to Mum in the background then he came back on. 'She said you'd had a breakdown and she'd helped you out. But then you got some drugs from someone and owed them money. She said she was scared for you, and that she wanted to help, so you weren't hurt in prison. I thought she was being nice.'

I felt like I was going to throw up. 'Dad, I'm so sorry. She obviously got your phone number from my diary, and now she's got money from you. Yes, I did have a breakdown, and I talked to Lisa a lot...but I did not take, or get drugs, or owe any money! That evil bitch stitched me up...'

Tears started to run down my face. I couldn't get my head around what she'd done. 'She's evil. Dad, I can't say I'm sorry enough.'

That phone call devastated me. *Why would Lisa have done that to me, and to my family?* I'd thought she was a friend who was occasionally moody, but now I knew she was a nasty manipulator. Conning me was one thing, but to do that to my sweet, naive, hardworking, honest dad was another.

February

I couldn't shake off my paranoia after that, and questioned everything. I didn't believe what people told me, and I felt deeply ashamed about what I'd put my parents through. I had to be harder, stronger, but still remain 'me'.

I felt like I was in mourning, I missed Jake that much. But I knew I'd be better off without him. *I'm stronger than him. I can go on alone.*

I spent a few weeks on the farm, which lifted my spirits and gave me hope.

It was hard, dirty work. I drove a tractor, milked the cows, and mucked them out. I even helped to deliver a calf! I became scared just once, when a cow ran at me. It nearly squashed me, and I ended up wetting my pants!

Regardless, I grew in confidence. I felt I could achieve things I wouldn't have previously attempted to do on my own.

March 2

That moment, when I was shouted for the bus to Askham, was one of the best of my life. When we got there, I thought we'd pulled up at a hotel.

I thought this would never happen. It's the beginning of the end.

The buildings at Askham were huge. It resembled a Tudor mansion, and was set in beautiful surround-ings. It held around 120 prisoners; I assumed this would make the atmosphere and routine less oppres-sive. *Fingers crossed.* The best part was how near it was to home – just a few miles.

March 4

The last stretch now... I could look to the future, now I was on the home run. A new life. I felt I could make it. I found ways to cope: I'd tick off a month at a time, after each menstrual period. If I concentrated on the month ahead, it encouraged me. *I might only be locked up for twelve more periods.* Then, hopefully, probation.

Positive thoughts came more frequently with spring in the air. The daily routine meant working outside in the garden; I also became an enthusiastic user of the gym, which boosted my fitness and gave me purpose.

I was understandably hesitant to befriend fellow prisoners, but eventually I became a mentor for others who found the system difficult. I'd never realised that I was skilled at listening to others. I almost felt back to normal, whatever that was.

I appreciated the wonderful family I had around me. I was always excited to see Elliot, James and Mum, but I was particularly thankful for two people in my life - the ones who had supported me through everything, and who I could never thank enough. They were my anchors, my rocks.

I was eternally grateful for my beautiful, level-head-ed, practical daughter. She sorted everything out for me, and did it with such grace and efficiency.

I also thanked God for my guiding light, my saviour, the one who led me through the darkness and who believed in me: my darling, amazing, generous dad.

With them behind me, I knew, without a shadow of a doubt, that I could start a new life. The day I'd walk through those prison gates for the last time couldn't come soon enough, but I was over the worst.

I'd learned my lesson, more than once. *Nothing in life comes easy – and if it does, it's because there are consequences attached.* I made a stupid decision, one that I wished I could change a million times, but I was paying my debt to society.

I planned to campaign against drugs on my release; I'd seen, first-hand, what they made people do, how they turned people into animals. I deeply regretted my part in that. *If I could change the life of someone who's mixed up with drugs...*

That would be my real penance – and the best way to pay back society for my crime.

My time in prison had been a living hell, and at times, I really didn't think I'd survive. I didn't think I had that much fight in me – I was a housewife from Yorkshire, not a streetwise chancer from the streets of London.

My experience taught me not to judge others, nor assume things about them. I'd certainly proved that stereotypes were false – I thought I could get away with a serious crime because I reckoned people wouldn't look at me twice. That 'anonymity' didn't stop me from being sentenced for five years.

That sentence will soon end, in the eyes of the law. But it will be something I'll carry with me for the rest of my days.

THE END